Buffy the Vampire Slayer™

The Script Book

Season Three, Volume 1

Pocket Books

New York London Toronto Sydney Singapore

Historian's Note: These teleplays represent the original shooting scripts for each episode; thus we have preserved any typos and misattributions. The scripts may include dialogue or even full scenes that were not in the final broadcast version of the show because they were cut due to length. Also, there may be elements in the broadcast that were added at a later date.

First Pocket Books edition July 2003

POCKET BOOKS
An imprint of Simon & Schuster
Africa House
64-78 Kingsway
London WC2B 6AH
www.simonsays.co.uk

Printed in the United States of America
10 9 8 7 6 5 4 3 2 1

ISBN 0-7434-6835-X

A CIP catalogue record for this book is available from the British Library

BUFFY THE VAMPIRE SLAYER

"Anne"

Written and Directed By

Joss Whedon

SHOOTING DRAFT

July 14, 1998   (WHITE)
July 15, 1998   (BLUE)
July 16, 1998   (PINK)

BUFFY THE VAMPIRE SLAYER

"Anne"

<u>CAST LIST</u>

BUFFY SUMMERS......................... Sarah Michelle Gellar
XANDER HARRIS......................... Nicholas Brendon
RUPERT GILES......................... Anthony S. Head
WILLOW ROSENBERG...................... Alyson Hannigan
CORDELIA CHASE........................ Charisma Carpenter
ANGEL................................. David Boreanaz
OZ.................................... Seth Green

JOYCE.................................
LARRY................................ Larry Bagby, III
LILY.................................. Julia Lee
RICKIE................................
KEN...................................* Carlos Jacott
JOAN..................................* Debra Christofferson
OLD WOMAN.............................* Barbara Pilavin
OLD MAN...............................* Harrison Young
ROUGHNECK.............................* Michael Leopard
TEACHER...............................* James Lurie
FIRST PRISONER........................
TRUCK GUY.............................* Dell Yount
DEMON GUARD...........................* Harley Zumbrum

*<u>OMITTED</u>
*JONATHAN..............................

BUFFY THE VAMPIRE SLAYER

"Anne"

SET LIST

INTERIORS

BUFFY'S APARTMENT
DINER
SUNNYDALE HIGH SCHOOL
     LIBRARY
     HALLWAY
THE BRONZE
BUFFY'S HOUSE
BLOODBANK
CONDEMNED BUILDING
     ANOTHER ROOM
FAMILY HOME/HELL
     MEETING ROOM
     CLEANSING CHAMBER
     DIMENSIONAL PORTAL CHAMBER
     MAIN CHAMBER
     CELL
     CHAMBER
*   SOME HALLWAY
*   CORRIDOR

EXTERIORS

GRAVEYARD
BEACH
STREET
*STREET BY DINER
ANOTHER STREET
HAMMERSMITH PARK

BUFFY THE VAMPIRE SLAYER

"Anne"

TEASER

1   EXT. GRAVEYARD - NIGHT   1

ANGLE: A GRAVESTONE

It reads: ANDREW HOELICH, 1981-1998.

And from the ground before it, a hand digs its way out of the grave.

The hand is, duh, Andrew's, and he pulls himself slowly up from under, vampire face in a grimace of effort.

A pair of legs steps into frame before him. Girl legs. From one of her hands dangles a wicked looking stake. Nearly all the way out, Andrew looks up at the figure facing him, grins.

> WILLOW
> That's right, big boy...

PUSH IN ON: WILLOW

Facing the vamp with a slayeresque 'tude.

> WILLOW (cont'd)
> Come and get it.

Andrew rises -- and Willow takes a step back, suddenly less Slayery. Andrew is about to move forward when XANDER **grabs** him from behind, wrapping his arms tight around him and spinning him to the right.

> XANDER
> I got him! Go!

OZ steps up from the shadows with a stake -- and pulls back to thrust it at the vamp.

> XANDER (cont'd)
> Any time now...

But Andrew suddenly kicks both legs up, slamming Oz in the jaw and sending him flying back, Andrew's legs continuing up until he flips himself over Xander, gets behind him. Xander spins, ready to fight, as Willow rushes forward to help. Andrew throws Xander into Willow and they both go sprawling. Andrew vaults over the tombstone and starts running away.

CONTINUED

1 CONTINUED: 1

                         WILLOW
              He's getting away. And, ow!

Suddenly Oz steps between the other two, an intense look of
cool concentration on his face.

ANGLE: THE STAKE

As he flips it, grabbing the pointy end and holding it
loosely at his finger tips.

ANGLE: ANDREW

Running away, his back presenting a dwindling target.

ANGLE: OZ

As he concentrates, lining up his shot.

In a blur, he suddenly HURLS the stake like a throwing knife.
It bounces uselessly off a tomb about eight feet away. Oz
shrugs.

                         OZ
              That really never works.
                    (turns to others)
              Are you guys all right?

                         WILLOW
              I can't believe he got away.

                         XANDER
              First of all, what was with the
              acrobatics? How did that happen?

                         OZ
              Wasn't Andy Hoelich on the gymnastics
              team?

                         XANDER
              That's right, he was!
                    (calls out after
                    Andrew)
              Cheater!

                         WILLOW
              That wasn't in the obituary. I
              should have checked the school
              records.

                                                        CONTINUED

1 CONTINUED: (2)   1

                    XANDER
          Okay, and the second problem I'm
          having...
                    (turns to Willow)
          "Come and get it big boy"?

                    WILLOW
                    (defensively)
          Well, well, the **slayer** always says a
          pun or a witty play on words and I
          think it throws vampires off and
          makes them frightened that I'm
          wisecracking and okay, I didn't
          really have time to work on that one
          but **you** try it every time!

                    OZ
          If I can suggest..."This times it's
          personal..."? I mean, there's a
          reason why it's a classic.

                    XANDER
          I was always amazed by the way Buffy
          fought, but... in a way I think we
          all took her punning for granted.

                    WILLOW
          Xander. Past Tense Rule.

                    XANDER
          Sorry. I just meant we in the past
          took it for granted and won't when
          she... when she comes back.

                    WILLOW
          Do you think she knows school's
          starting tomorrow?

                    OZ
          Tomorrow. Right. The big day.

                    WILLOW
                    (to comfort him)
          I'm gonna be busy a lot, but only
          till three and that's when you
          usually get up, so it's not bad.

                    OZ
                    (hiding something)
          Yeah...

                                                          CONTINUED

1   CONTINUED: (3)   1

                    XANDER
          I can't wait to see Cordelia. I
          can't believe I can't wait to see
          Cordelia.

                    WILLOW
               (excited)
          I wonder what our first homework
          assignment will be!
               (off Xander's look)
          Hey, you're excited about Cordelia,
          okay? We've all got issues.

                    OZ
          I guess we should pack it in.

                    XANDER
          Yeah...

They head toward the van.

                    WILLOW
          Wouldn't it be great if Buffy just
          showed up tomorrow? Like nothing
          happened?

                    XANDER
          She can't just show up. She was
          kicked out.

                    WILLOW
          Well, yeah, but... I just wish...
               (softly)
          I wish we knew where she was.

2   EXT. BEACH - SUNSET   2

The waves crash gloriously onto the bright and silent beach.
There is no one to be seen for miles around.

Till BUFFY walks into frame. She is walking slowly, in a
light sundress, bare feet digging into the sand. It's a warm
calming tableau and Buffy is soaking it up. She stops,
looking off into the distance.

CLOSE ON: BUFFY

As she shuts her eyes, letting the sun warm her face, the
camera tilts down her body to her midsection -- as two male
arms slide around her from behind. We tilt back up to see
ANGEL holding her, burying his face in her neck. She reaches
up behind her to caress his face.

                                                      CONTINUED

2 CONTINUED: 2

>   BUFFY
>   How did you find me here?
>
>   ANGEL
>   (intimately)
>   If I was blind, I would see you.
>
>   BUFFY
>   Stay with me.
>
>   ANGEL
>   Forever. That's the whole point.
>   I'll never leave.
>   (whispers)
>   Not even if you kill me.

3 INT. BUFFY'S APARTMENT - NIGHT   3

Where Buffy awakens suddenly, a screech and a siren heard
outside. We are close on her, pulling slowly back as she
gets wearily out of bed, a big tee shirt her sleeping gear.
As she walks slowly forward we continue to lead her, seeing
just a dark glimpse of a dingy, small apartment. We arm out
through the window as Buffy reaches it, leaning out and
looking down at her environs.

It ain't the beach, and it sure as hell isn't Sunnydale.

It's The City. Every city, the grimy back streets dotted
with the poor and the pro's. Sort of your worst nightmare of
where your kid might run away to.

Buffy leans on the windowsill and stares into the bleak urban
night.

>   BLACK OUT.

>   END OF TEASER

ACT ONE

4 INT. DINER - DAY   4

We see the bustle of midday lunch traffic. Track along
booths as a WAITRESS we can't see drops plates off at one
table and proceeds to another. A few ROUGHNECKS sit at it,
finishing their meal.

                    THE WAITRESS
          Anything else?

                    ROUGHNECK
          That'll do us, peaches.

ANGLE: THE WAITRESS'S NAME TAG

Says "ANNE". We tilt up from it to reveal that Anne is in
fact, Buffy. She rips off a bill and puts it on the table,
avoiding eye contact with the men (as she does with pretty
much everyone).

                    BUFFY
          Pay at the counter.

                    ROUGHNECK   *
                  (leering)
          Sure you don't want me to work it off?

Buffy turns away without comments and the man actually slaps
her ass.

DOLLY IN ON BUFFY

Her back to the camera, she turns slightly -- slayeresque
intent in her eyes. After a moment, it flickers and fades.
She moves on.

ANGLE: A NEARBY TABLE

There is a couple at the table, young and without means.
Neither of them is past twenty, both a bit strung out. But
clearly into each other, and very friendly. The boy is
RICKIE. The girl is LILY, though a few people might remember
her as Chantarelle in another life.

They are giggling, examining their forearms for some reason.

                    BUFFY
          Are you guys ready?

                    RICKIE
          Yeah, I think we're good, um...

                                              CONTINUED

9

4   CONTINUED: 4

He cranes to see the name tag.

                    RICKIE (cont'd)
          ...Anne.

                    BUFFY
          What'll you have?

                    RICKIE
          Well, okay...

He dumps a bunch of change onto the table, amounting to a
couple of dollars at most.

                    RICKIE (cont'd)
                    (counting the change)
          What can we get with this?

                    BUFFY
          Well...

                    LILY
          Can we get cake?

                    RICKIE
          Don't be stupid! We gotta eat
          healthy. Can't have cake.
                    (to Buffy)
          Can we get pie?

                    LILY
                    (good idea)
          That's better. That's got fruit.

                    BUFFY
          We got peach pie. I can't guarantee
          there's a peach in it...

                    LILY
          We shouldn't have blown all our money.

                    RICKIE
          It was worth it.
                    (to Buffy)
          Check this out.

He and Lily hold their forearms out together. They've
gotten two halves of a heart, his with 'Lily' in it and hers
with 'Rickie'. Put 'em together and they make a whole. The
work is a little primitive, which makes it all the more
endearing.

                                              CONTINUED

4   CONTINUED: (2)   4

                              BUFFY
                    It's nice. It's nice and...
                    permanent.

                              RICKIE
                    Yeah, well, forever. That's the
                    whole point.

Buffy looks up, startled at the echo of Angel's words. Lily
gets her first good look at Buffy.

                              LILY
                    Hey... do I know you?

                              BUFFY
                         (abrupt)
                    I don't think so.

                              LILY
                    Really? Where're you from?

                              BUFFY
                    I'll get your pie.

She takes off, Lily watching her with a quizzical expression.
After a moment she shrugs.

ANGLE: BUFFY

By the swinging doors to the kichen. She stops by another
waitress.

                              BUFFY (cont'd)
                    Can you cover my station for a while?
                    I'm not feeling great.

The waitress nods. Buffy looks briefly back at the couple,
who are smooching. Buffy exits.

5   INT. LIBRARY - DAY   5

(**WARNING:** if humanly possible, the next five pages -- scenes   *
5 through 7 -- will be done in **ONE SHOT**, moving from the   *
library to the cafeteria and capturing the vibrant cacophany   *
of the first day of school. You have been warned.)   *

For once, the library is full of STUDENTS. They mill about,
getting books, greeting each other, grabbing text books from
boxes on the tables.

Giles walks down the steps with Willow, in mid conversation.

                                                    CONTINUED

5   CONTINUED: 5

                              GILES
                    So, no joy in the cemetery?

                              WILLOW
                    No, he got away. We still have
                    glitches in the system, like vampires
                    getting away. But I think we're
                    improving.

          Giles goes around the counter as Willow stays on the civilian
          side. Giles checks out her books.   *

                              GILES
                    Well, for god's sake be careful. I
                    appreciate your efforts to keep the
                    vampire population down until Buffy
                    returns but if you should be
                    hurt or killed, I shall take it
                    somewhat amiss.

                              WILLOW
                    You'd be cranky.

                              GILES
                    Entirely.

          The phone rings in Giles' office.

                              WILLOW
                    Well, we try not to get killed.
                    That's part of our whole mission
                    statement. Don't get killed.

                              GILES
                    Good.
                         (re: the last book)
                    You're going to love this.

          He goes to answer the phone as Willow picks up her books and
          turns to go, seeing:

                              WILLOW
                    Hi!

                              CORDELIA
                    Hey, Willow.

          Cordelia comes up to Willow. They do an awkward almost-hug.

                              WILLOW
                    How was your summer?

                                                          CONTINUED

5 CONTINUED: (2)   5

                        CORDELIA
                   (putting her bag on
                   the counter while
                   she takes off her
                   jacket)
          I can't believe you brought that up.   *
          Las Palmas was the <u>nightmare</u> resort.
          They order you around, they make you
          have organized
                   (making quotemarks)
          "fun", and I make sarcastic
          quotemarks, plus the fact that there
          are cockroaches in Mexico big enough
          to own property. It was all about
          dread.

     They start heading out of the library into the --

6 INT. HALLWAY - DAY   6

                        CORDELIA
          So, how was your summer?

     Willow gets out about half a consonant before:

                        CORDELIA (cont'd)
          Is Xander here?

                        WILLOW
          Well, uh, yeah. Somewhere.

                        CORDELIA
                   (obviously excited)
          Good. Great. I haven't seen him
          yet. Do I look okay? How's my hair?

                        WILLOW
          It's good.

                        CORDELIA
          He didn't meet anybody over the
          summer, did he? No, this is
          Sunnydale, who could he meet except
          for monsters and stuff, then again
          he's always kind of attracted to
          monsters... How's my hair?

                        WILLOW
          Still good.
                   (looks off)
          Hi!

                                                     CONTINUED

13

6 CONTINUED: 6

                              CORDELIA
                         (fear)
                    Maybe he's forgotten me.
                         (lust)
                    Well, I'll make him remember. See ya.

Willow's attention is on the approaching figure. She
continues as Oz enters frame.

                              WILLOW
                    You came to visit me!
                         (puzzled)
                    You came with books.
                         (brightening)
                    Are they books for me?

                              OZ
                    Actually, they're kind of for me.

                              WILLOW
                    I don't get it.

                              OZ
                    Well, it's sort of a funny story.
                         (as they start up the
                          hall)
                    Remember when I didn't graduate?

                              WILLOW
                    Well, I know you had a lot of
                    incompletes, but that's why you had
                    summer school.

                              OZ
                    Yeah. Remember when I didn't go?

A bunch of kids run past them, laughing, passing a teacher:

                              TEACHER
                    Slow down, people! Summer's over.
                    Be somber.

Oz and Willow take over the frame again, continuing down the
hall.

                              WILLOW
                    But you never said anything. How am
                    I supposed to react to this rather
                    alarming news?

                              OZ
                    I was pretty much banking on you
                    finding it cute.

                                                      CONTINUED

                              14

6   CONTINUED: (2)   6

                         WILLOW
                Well, traditionally, repeating a
                grade is not a turn on. And you're
                practically a genius! You're Mister
                Test Scores! It's all a little weird.

                         OZ
                So the cute thing is out?

They enter the big lobby type area and Xander stops in front
of them. He's excited.

                         XANDER
                Have you guys seen Cordelia?

                         WILLOW
                She's here somewhere --

                         XANDER
                I don't want to come on too geeky.
                But, okay, I'm psyched. There's
                gonna be some heat, if you know what
                I mean. You guys might want to duck
                and cover. I'm starting to be geeky.
                Okay, bye.

He takes off, then reappears.

                         XANDER (cont'd)
                How --

                         WILLOW
                Your hair's fine.

                         XANDER
                Cool.

He takes off -- and then LARRY passes, talking to another   *
JOCK.   *

                         LARRY   *
                This is our year, I'm telling you.   *
                Best football season ever. I'm so in   *
                shape, I'm a rock -- it's all about   *
                egg whites -- we got Garrity at   *
                running back, Dale at QB, if we can   *
                focus, keep discipline and not have   *
                quite as many mysterious deaths,   *
                Sunnydale is gonna RULE.   *

We pick up Oz and Willow again, still dealing with their
little issue.

                                                        CONTINUED

6   CONTINUED: (3)   6

                         WILLOW
          I'm trying to get to cute, really,
          but I'm still sorta stuck on
          "strange."

                         OZ
          Okay, well, I'd be willing to bargain
          down to "eccentric" with an option on
          "cool".

                         WILLOW
          Let me sleep on it, you know, and
          we'll get back to you.

The camera follows another student to the lounge, where we
find Xander and Cordelia finally greeting each other.

                         XANDER
          Hey.

                         CORDELIA
          Hey.

                         XANDER
          Good summer?

                         CORDELIA
          It was all right.

                         XANDER
          Cool.

                         CORDELIA
          Yeah.

                         XANDER
          I'll see you.

                         CORDELIA
          Yeah, whatever.

They split in different directions, both wildly unsatisfied
with that exchange. Xander is swept along into a group of
STUDENTS heading loudly into the cafeteria as we --

                                             SMASH CUT TO:

7   INT. BUFFY'S APARTMENT - DAY   7

Dead silence. No movement. Buffy sits on the bed, a half
opened can of spaghetti-o's with a can opener in her hand.

                                             CONTINUED

7   CONTINUED: 7

The light is mostly from the one bulb, and it's
pretty bleak.

Buffy never moves.

8   EXT. STREET BY DINER - DAY   8   *

Buffy walks along in her waitress uniform, a coat over it.
Heading for work. She silently takes in the urban tableaux
around her. A clean cut young man, KEN, is handing a leaflet
to a YOUNG RUNAWAY. A crazy OLD WOMAN is huddled in the
corner, swaying and mumbling.

As Buffy passes her, the old woman looks at her and says:

                    OLD WOMAN
          I'm no one... I'm no one...

Buffy keeps walking, enters the diner.   *

9   INT. LIBRARY - AFTER SCHOOL (DAY)   9

Giles is on the phone in his office.

                    GILES
          Yes, thank you.

He hangs up and comes out into the library where Xander and
Willow are looking over their new books.

                    GILES (cont'd)
          I have a lead. A friend in Oakland
          has a sketchy report of a girl
          fending off a group of vampires a
          week ago. There's a flight out in an
          hour.

                    XANDER
          And what makes this different from
          the last nine leads?

                    GILES
          Well, I believe there is a meal on
          this flight

There is a bit of defeat in his voice.

                                                          CONTINUED

9   CONTINUED: 9

                              XANDER
                    I don't mean to poop the party, it's
                    just, you get hopes all up and then
                    it's just a big fat raspberry and I feel
                    bad.

                              WILLOW
                    It's still good that you're looking,
                    though. You shouldn't give up.

                              XANDER
                    Oh, yeah. Definitely.

                              GILES
                    Well, one must try. In the meantime,
                    you might want to take a slight
                    vacation from your slaying.

                              WILLOW
                    Hey, we're doing okay.
                              (bitterly)
                    Except that last guy totally threw
                    off our stats...

                              GILES
                    I just don't want you getting into
                    trouble while I'm away. I should go.

He takes off. The kids watch him go.

                              WILLOW
                    You don't think maybe he'll find her?

                              XANDER
                    I think he'll find her when she wants
                    to be found.

10   EXT. STREET - NIGHT   10   *

Buffy walks quietly by herself, a coat over her waitress   *
outfit. Returning from work.

Lily appears behind her, catches up, calling to her.   *

                              LILY
                    Anne? Anne?

Buffy doesn't notice.

                              LILY (cont'd)
                    Buffy?

                                                       CONTINUED

10 CONTINUED: 10

Buffy stops, turns.

                    LILY (cont'd)
          Don't be mad. I won't turn you in or
          nothing. I guess you don't recognize
          me.

                    BUFFY
          Lily?

                    LILY
          I mean from before. I was calling
          myself Chantarelle then. I used to..
          I was in that cult that worshipped
          vampires.
                    (rolls her eyes)
          So lame, I know...

                    BUFFY
          Oh, yeah...

                    LILY
          You kind of saved us. I never
          thanked you or anything.

                    BUFFY
          Did you tell anyone who I was?

                    LILY
          Oh, no! Not even Ricky. I was so
          surprised to see you here, waiting
          tables... but I wouldn't tell. I
          know how it is when you gotta get
          lost.

They fall into step together.

                    BUFFY
          So, you live nearby?

                    LILY
          There's a couple of places, they're
          abandoned and a lot of people stay
          there. Ricky knows all those places,
          he can always find somewhere to
          crash. He's pretty smart. So how
          come you came up with Anne?

                    BUFFY
          It's my middle name.

                                                    CONTINUED

10 CONTINUED: (2)   10

                         LILY
          Lily's from a song. Ricky picked it.
          I'm always changing anyway.
          Chantarelle was part of my exotic
          phase.

                         BUFFY
          It's nice. It's a mushroom.

                         LILY
          It is? That's really embarassing.

                         BUFFY
          It's an exotic mushroom, if that's
          any comfort.

                         LILY
          Well, before that I was following
          this loser Preacher and calling
          myself Sister Sunshine. There's
          nothing worse than that.

                         BUFFY
          Nothing springs to mind, it's
          true.... What about at home, what'd
          they call you?

Lily doesn't answer -- home not a welcome concept, and Buffy
realizes it.

                         BUFFY (cont'd)
          Well, I like Lily.

                         LILY
          It's cool for now. Hey, do you have
          any money?

Buffy stops, not sure what to say.

                         LILY (cont'd)
          I don't mean that like... Well, I
          just mean, I know a guy, he's having
          like a rave kind of thing, in this
          basement, it's three dollars to get
          in and you have to know someone. We
          could go, I could show you if you
          had... 'cause I'm broke.

                         BUFFY
          I don't think so. I kind of want to
          be alone.

                                                          CONTINUED

                              20

10 CONTINUED: (3)   10

                         LILY
                    (hurt)
               Well, I didn't mean to bug you...

                         BUFFY
               No, I just mean a lot of people would
               be too much.
                    (digs into pocket)
               Here, why don't you go with Rickie,
               and I'll see you some time --

                         LILY
               No, that's okay, forget about it.

                         BUFFY
               No, really, I --

An OLD MAN ploughs through them.

                         BUFFY (cont'd)
               Whoah!

                         LILY
               That's not very polite.

The old man turns and looks at the two girls. Horror fills
his eyes.

                         BUFFY
               Are you okay?

He just stares, finally emitting a cracked whisper:

                         OLD MAN
               I'm no one...

                         BUFFY
               What?

The old man looks at them a moment more, then steps into the   *
street -- right in front of an oncoming pick-up.

Without hesitation, Buffy bolts, running right into the
street and pushing the old man out of the way.

The truck slams into her. She flies back and hits the ground
just as hard.

                                             BLACK OUT.

               END OF ACT ONE

                                                  CONTINUED

                              21

ACT TWO

11
EXT. STREET - NIGHT   11

Lily rushes over to Buffy, who is just getting up. The
DRIVER of the truck also gets out, comes up to her.

                         LILY
              Are you okay?

                         TRUCK GUY
              Jeez, I didn't see you!   *

                         LILY
              Maybe you shouldn't move...

But Buffy is standing, albeit a bit unsteadily.

                         TRUCK GUY
              Yeah, you should lie down. Somebody
              call an ambulance!

                         BUFFY
              It's okay...

But more PEOPLE are starting to crowd around. Buffy looks
about her, unease rising.

                         BUFFY (cont'd)
              I have to go...

And she takes off, running down the street and disappearing
around the corner.

                         TRUCK GUY
              You sure you don't want to sue?   *

12
EXT. ANOTHER STREET - CONTINUOUS - NIGHT   12

Buffy rounds the corner and runs right into Ken. His
leaflets fly everywhere.

                         KEN
              Whoah! Where are you running to?

Buffy starts picking up leaflets.

                         BUFFY
              I'm sorry...

                                                          CONTINUED

12 CONTINUED: 12

                          KEN
              Maybe I should ask, where are you
              running **from**.

Buffy hesitates, then continues picking up leaflets. Ken
squats, helps.

                          KEN (cont'd)
              You're pretty new around here.
              You've got the look, though.

                          BUFFY
              The look.

                          KEN
              Like you had to grow up way too fast.
              What's your name?

Buffy hands him the flyers.

                          BUFFY
              Anne.

                          KEN
              I'm Ken. Go ahead and keep one of
              these.

He hands her back a flyer.

ANGLE: THE FLYER

Says FAMILY HOME on it.

                          KEN (cont'd)
              Don't be shy about stopping by. I
              guess you're not starving, but we're
              not just interested in feeding the
              body. You might find something
              you're missing.

                          BUFFY
              I'm all right.

                          KEN
              Then why are you here?

She doesn't answer. He looks over at a couple of KIDS
hanging out.

                          KEN (cont'd)
              This isn't a good place for a kid to
              be. You get old fast here.
                          (more)

                                                   CONTINUED

12   CONTINUED: (2)   12

                              KEN (cont'd)
                    The thing that does it, that drains
                    the life out of them: despair. Kids
                    come here, they got nothing to go
                    home to and this is the last stop for
                    a lot of them. Shouldn't have to be
                    that way.

As Buffy looks at the kids as well we hear a SONG start on
the soundtrack, seeing various angles of kids on the street:

-- Kids begging

-- a Kid buying drugs

-- Kids hanging out

-- Kids getting into a fight as Buffy walks by, heading for
home and the song continues as we --

                                                  CUT TO:

13   INT. THE BRONZE - NIGHT   13

And we see the band singing the song we've been listening to.
It's a slow, somber ballad, and the mood in the joint matches
it.

Xander, Oz, and Willow are sitting at a table, watching the
stage. Kinda low.

                              XANDER
                    Boy, I'm glad we showed up for
                    "Depressing Night."

                              WILLOW
                    I wonder what she's doing right now.

                              XANDER
                    Oh, I know what she's doing. Gabbing
                    to all her friends about her
                    passionate affair with Pedro the
                    cabana boy and laughing about me
                    thinking she might still care about
                    me.
                         (off Willow's look)
                    It's possible you were talking about
                    Buffy.

                                                  CONTINUED

13 CONTINUED: 13

                         WILLOW
                It's possible.
                     (looking around)
                The Bronze just never seems the
                same without her.

                         XANDER
                The slaying isn't getting any easier,
                either.

                         OZ
                I think we're getting a rhythm down.

                         XANDER
                We're losing half the vamps.

                         OZ
                Yeah, but, rhythmically.

                         WILLOW
                Oh! That reminds me.
                     (pulls out a folded
                     up piece of paper)
                I asked around about Andrew Hoelich,
                our gymnastic vampire, and apparently,
                     (looking at her notes)
                he used to like to hang out in
                Hammersmith Park and pick up grills!
                     (looks closer)
                Or, okay, that could be "girls".

                         XANDER
                Let's hope.

                         OZ
                Are we thinking old habits die hard?

                         XANDER
                Worth checking out.

                         WILLOW
                Tomorrow night?

                         XANDER
                Good. And this time we'll be ready
                for him. Take him out before he does
                a Kerri Strug on your face.

        Xander notices as:

        ANGLE: CORDELIA

        Walks in with some friends.

                                                          CONTINUED

13 CONTINUED: (2)   13

                         WILLOW
                 We just need to work on our timing,
                 I think.

                         XANDER
                 No, I know what we need.

                         OZ
                 A vampire slayer?   *

                         XANDER
                 Next best thing. Bait.

14 INT. DINER - DAY   14

        Buffy is in the middle of her shift as Lily enters, a bit
        distraught.

                         LILY
                 Buf -- uh, Anne? Can I talk to you?

        Buffy leads her over to one side.

                         BUFFY
                 We got kind of a rush here, is there
                 another time --

                         LILY
                 Rickie's gone. I mean, I haven't
                 seen him for more than a day, he's
                 never left for that long, I think
                 something's happened. Maybe
                 something's happened.

                         BUFFY
                 Well, did you talk to the police?

                         LILY
                     (shaking her head)
                 Rickie's skipped on his parole,
                 they'd just...

                         BUFFY
                 Well, you could... I don't know, ask
                 around and --

                         LILY
                 Can you help me?

        Buffy looks at her a moment.

                                                      CONTINUED

14   CONTINUED: 14

                         BUFFY
               I can't.

                         LILY
               But, but, that's who you are and
               stuff, right? I mean, you help
               people... and, you know...

                         BUFFY
               I can't get into this now, I'm
               sorry...

                         LILY
               You know how to do stuff...

                         BUFFY
               I can't; not anymore...

                         LILY
                    (near tears)
               But... I don't know what to do...

Buffy doesn't answer for a moment. There is no relish in her
voice as she offers:

                         BUFFY
               I'm off at four.

15   INT. BUFFY'S HOUSE - AFTERNOON (DAY)   15

Joyce sits in the living room, doing bills. The doorbell
rings and her head snaps up. She moves quickly to the door,
opening it to reveal Giles.

She lets the tide of disappointment settle, greets him.

                         JOYCE
               Mr. Giles. Hello.

                         GILES
               Hello. May I --

                         JOYCE
               Of course. Come on in.

They head back to the living room.

                         GILES
               I've just come from Oakland. A
               friend of mine called with a lead.
               Stories about someone fighting
               vampires.

                                                      CONTINUED

15 CONTINUED: 15

Joyce turns, a moment of painful hope.

                    GILES (cont'd)
          It didn't pan out, I'm afraid.

                    JOYCE
          No Buffy.

                    GILES
          No vampires. Bunch of school kids in
          heavy mascara listening to extremely
          silly music.

                    JOYCE
          Well, thank you for going. I can't
          even... I can hardly leave the house.
          I'm so afraid that she'll call, that
          she'll... need help...

                    GILES
          Buffy is the most capable child I
          have ever known. She may be
          confused, unhappy, but I honestly
          believe she's in no danger.

                    JOYCE
          I just wish I could talk to her. The
          last thing we did was fight...

                    GILES
          Joyce, you mustn't blame yourself for
          Buffy's leaving.

                    JOYCE
          I don't...
                    (looking him in the
                    eye)
          I blame you.

This makes her as uncomfortable as it does him, but she
doesn't back down.

                    JOYCE (cont'd)
          You've been this huge influence in
          her life, guiding her -- you've had
          this whole relationship behind my
          back that I... I feel like you've
          taken her away from me.

                    GILES
          I... I didn't make Buffy who she is.

                                              CONTINUED

28

15   CONTINUED: (2)   15

                    JOYCE
          And who exactly is she?

He does not answer.

16   INT. BLOODBANK - AFTERNOON (DAY)   16

A largish, dingy room. There are dentist chairs in a row at
the back -- a couple of people are giving blood in them. A
counter with a phone, filing cabinet etc. near the door. A
worker, JOAN, late thirties, attends to one of the DONORS.

Buffy and LILY enter, looking about.

                    LILY
          We gave blood a lot of times 'cause
          you get a few bucks and they have
          cookies.

                    BUFFY
          You're a fan of the sugar rush,
          aren't you?

                    LILY
          It's nice.

                    JOAN
               (crossing to them)
          Hi. Are you here to donate blood?   *

                    BUFFY
          Oh, no. I mean, I can't. Needles.
          They make me woozy. Which is weird,
          'cause I don't have a problem with
          battle axes, but needles...
               (recovers herself)
          we're looking for a friend.

                    LILY
          Rickie T? We come in sometimes...

                    JOAN
          Rickie, sure. He's not here...

                    BUFFY
          Has he been in, do you know? In the
          last day or so?

                    JOAN
          Let me check the sheet.

She goes off a bit to do so.

                                                        CONTINUED

16 CONTINUED: 16

                    BUFFY
          This'll probably go faster if we
          split up.

                    LILY
          Can I come with you?

                    BUFFY
          Okay, when did I lose you on the
          whole splitting up thing?

                    LILY
          Sorry.   *

                    BUFFY
          We can both check out some of your   *
          hangouts and meet later. At my   *
          place.   *
                                                      *

                    LILY
          Okay.   *

                    JOAN
                (returning)
          Sorry, guys. He hasn't been here.

                    BUFFY
          Thanks.

                    JOAN
          I'll tell him you were looking...

     The girls go, Buffy handing Lily a key.   *

                    BUFFY   *
          This is for the downstairs...   *

     Joan watches them, the smile draining from her face.   *

17 INT. CONDEMNED BUILDING - NIGHT   17

     Buffy enters the building slowly, looking around. It's a
     grimy, torn up place. Alien to her. No lights -- just
     moonlight through the broken or boarded up windows.

     She makes her way from one room to the next -- stepping over
     a few SLEEPING PEOPLE, looking to make sure none is Rickie.
     none is, and she continues to move through the darkness.

     A figure suddenly moves at her -- and OLD WINO, who glares at
     her. She moves on.

18   INT. ANOTHER ROOM - A BIT LATER (NIGHT)   18

She makes her way in through a hole in the wall. Moves
forward, then stops.

ANGLE: THE OLD MAN

Who walked in front of the pick up. He lies very dead in the
corner. An open bottle of drain cleaner beside him.

                         BUFFY
                Oh, god...

She moves to his side, grabbing his wrist to take his pulse.
None.

She stops, his wrist still in her hands. Stares down at his
arm.

ANGLE: HIS ARM

Bears a tattoo. Half a heart, with the name LILY in the
middle.

                         BUFFY (cont'd)
                Rickie...

                                              BLACK OUT.

             END OF ACT TWO

ACT THREE

19

INT. BUFFY'S APARTMENT - NIGHT   19

Lily is sitting on the bed, rises as Buffy enters.

                    LILY
          Did you find Rickie?

Buffy takes off her coat.

                    LILY (cont'd)
          I thought of, he likes to go to this
          movie house, you can get in the
          back --

                    BUFFY
          Lily, I think... that he's dead.

Lily takes this in, eyes brimming.

                    LILY
          But... he takes care of me...

21   BUFFY
          I'm sorry...

                    LILY
          We're gonna get a place, his cousin
          could get him a job at the car wash...

                    BUFFY
          Lily. Something's happening. The
          person I found was old, he looked
          about eighty --

                    LILY
          Well, that's not Rickie --

                    BUFFY
          I'm sure it was. Lily, something
          drained the life out of him. Made
          him old. I don't know how, but...
          there could be something out there.

                    LILY
          Do you mean, like a vampire?

                    BUFFY
              (thinking it through)
          They wouldn't accelerate the aging
          process, but maybe...
              (more)

                                                          CONTINUED

19   CONTINUED: 19

                         BUFFY (cont'd)
          maybe something in his blood... When
          was the last time you guys gave blood
          together?

                         LILY
          I don't understand... maybe it's not
          Rickie, okay?

                         BUFFY
          Lily. You have to deal with this.

                         LILY
          But he didn't do anything wrong, why
          would --

                         BUFFY
          That's not the point. These things
          happen, you can't close your eyes and
          hope they'll go away.

                         LILY
          It is 'cause of you?

                         BUFFY
          What?

                         LILY
          You know about... monsters and stuff,
          you could have brought this with
          you...

                         BUFFY
                    (snapping)
          I didn't bring anything with me! And
          I didn't ask for you to come to me
          with your problems. I just wanted to
          be left alone. If you can't deal
          with what's happening, don't lay it
          off on me --

Lily rises, she really CAN'T deal, she's out the door.

                         BUFFY (cont'd)
          Lily --

But she makes no move to stop her. Stands in the middle of
the room, fuming. After a moment her anger deflates. She
looks to the door -- what should she do?

20 EXT. STREET - NIGHT   20

Lily is crying, moving down the street. A figure approaches
from the darkness. It's Ken.

                    KEN
              Are you okay?

She just shakes her head.

                    KEN (cont'd)
              Hey, it's okay. Maybe I can help.

                    LILY
              You can't.

                    KEN
              I know you all think I'm a big
              square, handing out leaflets about
              hope. But hope is a real thing, just
              like despair. Hope can fill up the
              part of you that's missing.

                    LILY
              But... Rickie...

                    KEN
              Rickie? Say, are you Lily? Right,
              he was talking about you.

                    LILY
              You've seen Rickie?

                    KEN
              Well, sure. Rickie's with us now.

                    LILY
              She said he was dead...

                    KEN
              Well, someone sure handed you a
              tall tale. Rickie's no more dead
              than I am. Why don't you come to
              Family Home. And we'll get you taken
              care of.

                    LILY
              Okay.

He is all gentle smiles as he leads her away.

21 INT. BLOODBANK - NIGHT   21

     The door is forced open by Buffy, who enters into darkness.
     JUMP CUT to her snooping about, looking over the chairs.
     JUMP CUT to her behind the counter, looking through files by
     the light of a lighter. She rifles through several, finds:

     ANGLE: RICKIE'S FILE

     A glance down it finds a great deal of information:

     ADDRESS: NONE

     FAMILY: NONE

     AILMENTS OR PRE-EXISTING MEDICAL CONDITIONS: NONE

     And at the bottom, a box marked COMMENTS with one word hand
     written in it:

     CANDIDATE

                         BUFFY
                    Candidate for what?

     The lights go on and Joan steps out from the back of the
     office. She eyes Buffy warily. Buffy looks at her.

                         JOAN
                    What are you doing?

                         BUFFY
                         (looking at the file)
                    Breaking into your office and looking
                    through your private files.
                    Candidate for what?

                         JOAN
                    I'm calling the police.

     Joan moves forward -- Buffy doesn't even look as she pulls
     the phone jack out of the wall. She looks over several files.

                         BUFFY
                    You've got a whole bunch of
                    candidates here. I wonder if any of
                    these kids are missing like Rickie.
                    Gosh I'll be they are.

                         JOAN
                    You're gonna get yourself in a lot of
                    trouble.

     Buffy puts the files down, faces Joan.

                                                    CONTINUED

21   CONTINUED: 21

                         BUFFY
              I don't want any trouble. I just want
              to be alone and quiet, you know, with
              a chair, and a fireplace, and a tea
              cozy. I'm not even sure what a tea
              cozy is, but I want one. Instead, I
              get trouble. Which I am willing to
              share. What are you doing to these
              kids?

                         JOAN
              Nothing! I just... give him names.
              He likes to know who... I give him
              the names of the healthy ones.

                         BUFFY
                    (steely eyed)
              Give them to who?
                    (beat)
              Or, wait -- give them to **whom?** Or
              maybe it's who...

                                        SMASH CUT TO:

22   INT. FAMILY HOME MEETING ROOM - NIGHT   22

A small, bare living room with a couch and a few hard backed
chairs in a circle. The front door leads out into the city,
but the windows are curtained off.

We are **on Ken** as he speaks to Lily.

                         KEN
              Well, don't you look nice.

She is wearing a plain shift of a dress, and is a little
uncomfortable in it.

                         LILY
              I guess...

                         KEN
              Well you don't want to wear your own
              outfit for the cleansing. It'll get
              soaked.

He leads her toward a door in the back.

                         LILY
              A cleansing is like a baptism, right?

                                             CONTINUED

22 CONTINUED: 22

                    KEN
          Not quite the same.

                    LILY
          And will I see Rickie after?

                    KEN
          Of course. He's waiting for you.
          He's very excited.

23 EXT. HAMMERSMITH PARK - NIGHT   23

The trio is leading Cordelia into the park. She is less than
enthused.

                    CORDELIA
          Why do I have to be bait? I'm always
          bait! Let Willow be bait.

                    XANDER
          He's already seen Willow. And could
          you complain louder, so that all the
          vampires leave?

                    OZ
          I think this is a good spot. Is
          everybody packing?

Xander and Willow show their weapons.

                    OZ (cont'd)
          Let's do it.

The three all move to separate hiding spots behind trees or
bushes. Cordelia spins, at a loss, then follows Xander. She
starts arguing again, at a whisper.

                    CORDELIA
          I only offered to help for Buffy's
          sake. It had nothing to do with you.

                    XANDER
          Yeah, like I needed **that** cleared up.
          Go away. This is my hiding spot.

                    CORDELIA
          Well, where do I hide?

                    XANDER
          You don't hide! You're bait! Go act
          baity.

                                                         CONTINUED

23   CONTINUED: 23

                         CORDELIA
               What's the plan?

                         XANDER
               The vampire attacks you.

                         CORDELIA
               And then what?

                         XANDER
               The vampire kills you. We watch. We
               rejoice.

ANGLE: WILLOW

Is rolling her eyes at this clearly audible exchange.

                         CORDELIA (O.S.)
               Everything's a joke to you.

                         XANDER (O.S.)
               No, just our relationship.

                         CORDELIA (O.S.)
               What relationship?

                         XANDER (O.S.)
               Oh, sorry, we want to bury that piece
               of the past, don't we...

As it continues, Andrew drifts out of the darkness behind
Willow. Hungry.

24   INT. CLEANSING CHAMBER - NIGHT   24

It's a small room with a couple of steps leading down to a
stone floor. It is somewhat dark, religious in feel but not
overtly creepy. In the center of the floor is what looks
like a really tiny lap pool -- a rectangle of maybe four by
eight feet filled with black, murky liquid.

Ken leads Lily to the edge of the pool.

                         KEN
               We come to this station to wash away
               the past. Go ahead and kneel. We
               let the water run over the sin, and
               the pain, and the uncertainty.

                         LILY
               It looks kind of dirty...

                                                    CONTINUED

24 CONTINUED: 24

Ken just smiles. He kneels to her side, waiting.

Lily reaches for the water, to splash it on her face.

25 INT. FAMILY HOME MEETING ROOM - NIGHT   25

Buffy is talking her way in, to a FAMILY HOME MEMBER. He is
as large and thuggish as the one next to him, or she probably
wouldn't be talking at all.

                    BUFFY
          You know, I just looked in the mirror
          and thought, hey! What's with all
          the sin? I need to change. I'm
          dirty, I'm bad... with the sex, and
          the... envy, and that loud music we
          kids listen to nowadays...

It's possible they're not buying this.

                    BUFFY (cont'd)
          I just suck at undercover. Where's
          Ken?

One of them starts to close the door -- and Buffy shoves it
wide open, sending him tumbling.

26 INT. CLEANSING CHAMBER - NIGHT   26

Lily reaches into the water, her hands gliding in,
disappearing up to the elbow.

Buffy throws the door open. Ken moves between her and Lily.

                    KEN
          This is a private moment, if you
          could just --

                    BUFFY
          How do you make 'em old, Ken? You
          feed on youth, what's the deal?

Ken drops his fascade as easily as Buffy dropped hers.

                    KEN
          Do you really want to know?

                    LILY
          What's going on?

                                                        CONTINUED

26   CONTINUED: 26

                              BUFFY
                Lily?

Lily's hand still trails in the water -- and she is suddenly
yanked in -- screaming as she disappears below the surface.

Buffy runs to her, but Ken blocks the way. Buffy tries to
throw him, but he is strong, locking her arms in his grip.
After a moment of struggle, Buffy just throws all her weight
into him and they both fall, wrapped like lovers, into the
liquid as well.   *

27   INT. DIMENSIONAL PORTAL CHAMBER - CONTINUOUS - NIGHT   27

Buffy and Ken come out the other side. That is, they fall
out of an identical pool that happens to be on the ceiling of
this small stone chamber. They hit the ground hard -- but   *
dry --, roll and separate. Buffy looks around.   *
                                                                *
                              BUFFY
                Lily?

Lily is on the ground nearby, groggy. She groans and stirs.
Buffy looks up.

ANGLE: THE POOL

Sits placidly above her with Escheresque improbability.

                              KEN
                My face... Ow, my face...

He has his back to us, clutches his head. Fury mounts in his
voice as he rises --

                              KEN (cont'd)
                Do you have any idea how hard it is
                to **glue that thing on?**

-- and spins, revealing his human face hanging limply in his
hands. The demon face beneath is glistening and scarred.
Just yucky. Plus the guy is seething with anger, staring at
Buffy hatefully.

                              KEN (cont'd)
                Guards!

FIGURES start running toward them from the shadows --
blocking access to the portal. A cursory glance reveals
their faces to be about as attractive as Ken's.

                                                      CONTINUED

27 CONTINUED: 27

Still not completely on top of what's going on, Buffy
nonetheless takes action. She scrambles toward Lily, helping
her up --

                         BUFFY
                  Lily! Come on!

-- and heading her down a corridor.

Ken grabs a nasty looking cudgel off one of the guards, heads
after the girls, but more slowly.

28 INT. CORRIDOR - CONTINUOUS - NIGHT   28   *

Buffy drags Lily along the corridor.

                         BUFFY
                  We gotta find another exit, there's
                  gotta be...

Yeah, she stops talking, as the corridor ends at a sheer
ledge, looking down at:

29 INT. MAIN CHAMBER - CONTINUOUS - NIGHT   29

It's enormous. And it's Hell. Part factory, part prison
camp, with more than a little Spanish Inquisition thrown in.
HUMAN PRISONERS work at hauling enormous stones, doing metal
work, any and all demeaning and backbreaking labour. Along
the tops of the huge concrete pillars, people have been hung
up to die for crimes of one kind or another. Molten metal
runs along gutters into metal vats. Everything is covered
with a layer of grime. Carey and David K blow their entire
budgets for the year, and Gareth can be seen in the corner
weeping.

The people all wear the same kind of nondescript outfit that
Lily has been put into, only dirtier. They are practically
zombies, submissive and silent. Guards -- demons all --
patrol around, occasionally stopping to beat a prisoner.
Their garb has a flavor of the medieval mixed in with the
SS.
It's all bad.

Searchlights at either end constantly sweep the place.

Buffy stops, taking it all in. Ken steps up behind her, in
control, since she has nowhere to run.

                         KEN
                  Welcome to my world. I hope you
                  like it.

                                                      CONTINUED

29 CONTINUED: 29

Buffy turns, confusion and horror on her face.

                          KEN (cont'd)
               You're never leaving.

He smashes the cudgel across her face and we --

                                              BLACK OUT.

                    END OF ACT THREE

ACT FOUR

30 EXT. HAMMERSMITH PARK - NIGHT   30

Xander and Cordy are still going at it.

                    XANDER
          Let me just ask you one thing. How
          long did it take you to forget me?
          Were you still taxiing on the runway,
          or was it actually in the cab?

                    CORDELIA
          Oh, yeah, like you were Mr. Faithful.
          Probably met some hot little inca
          mummy girl -- yeah, I heard about
          her --

Xander motions for her to be quiet. There is a rustling
sound from nearby. Twigs snapping, a fall.

                    WILLOW (O.S.)
          HELP!

They bolt for Willow's hiding space -- but Oz zips by them,
already up to speed.

ANGLE: WILLOW

Is struggling with Andrew. Oz tackles him, but Andrew is
back on his feet in a second, takes off.

He runs into Xander and takes him to the ground.

                    CORDELIA
          Xander!

She leaps on Andrew's back, pulling at him as Xander shoves
his stake through Andrew's heart.

Andrew explodes into dust, which drops Cordy right on top of
Xander. Without hesitation, they commence kissing.

31 INT. CELL - LATER (NIGHT)   31

Buffy more or less wakens. She sees Lily sitting with her
back to the wall, terror on her face.

The Cell is dark, with a stone floor and a latticed iron
grill at one wall. The girls share the cell with two
others -- a SIXTYSOMETHING MAN who is entirely beyond speech
or reason, and a DECAYING CORPSE.

                                                    CONTINUED

31 CONTINUED: 31

                         BUFFY
               Lily...?

Just the effort of speaking makes Buffy's head hurt even
more. She tries to sit up, takes it slow.

                         LILY
               I always knew I would come here...
               sooner or later... I knew I belonged
               here...

                         BUFFY
               Where?

                         LILY
                    (looking at Buffy)
               Hell.

                         BUFFY
               This... isn't Hell...

                         KEN
               Isn't it?

He paces just behind the bars, grinning at the girls as he
speaks.

                         KEN (cont'd)
               What is Hell, but the total absence
               of Hope? The substance, the tactile
               proof of despair? You're right,
               Lily. This is where you've been
               heading all your life. You come from
               nothing, to become nothing.

                         BUFFY
               Don't listen to him...

But Lily is rapt, and Buffy is too weak and bewildered to
present much of a counter argument.

                         KEN
               Just like Rickie.

                         LILY
               Rickie...

                         KEN
               He forgot you. It took a long
               time -- he remembered your name years
               after he'd forgotten his own. But in
               the end...

                                                          CONTINUED

31 CONTINUED: (2)   31

                         LILY
              Years? But...

                         KEN
              Time here moves more quickly than in
              your dimension. A hundred long years
              will pass here -- on Earth, just a
              day.

                         BUFFY   *
              So you work us till we're too old,   *
              then spit us back out.   *

                         KEN
              Very good.   *
                    (to Lily)   *
              You see, Lily, you'll die of old age   *
              before anyone wonders where you went.   *
              Not that anyone will. That's why we   *
              chose you.

                         BUFFY
              You didn't choose me.

                         KEN
              No, but I know you, "Anne." So
              afraid, so pathetically determined to
              run away from whatever you used to   *
              be. To disappear. Congratulations.
              You got your wish.

         Buffy glares at him, hating him, hating the truth of his
         words.

32 INT. CHAMBER - LATER (NIGHT)   32

         It's a dark room with old, iron metalwork and machines lining
         the walls.

         Buffy is thrown to the ground by a couple of DEMON GUARDS as
         a third addresses a cluster of SEVEN PRISONERS, including
         Lily and Buffy.

         Buffy stands, still shaky.

                         DEMON GUARD
              You work, and you live. That is all.
              You do not complain, or laugh, or do
              anything besides work. Whatever you
              thought, whatever you were, does not
              matter. You are no one now, you mean
              nothing.

                                                     CONTINUED

32 CONTINUED: 32

He approaches the first prisoner, a boy of eighteen.

                    DEMON GUARD (cont'd)
          Who are you?

                    FIRST PRISONER
                  (terrified)
          Aaron...

The guard swings his club with deadly speed and smashes the
boy to the ground.

Buffy shakes off the last of her grogginess. Gets that look.

The guard moves to the second prisoner. Lily.

                    DEMON GUARD
          Who are you?

                    LILY
          No one.

The guard smiles, moves on.

                    DEMON GUARD
          Who are you?

                    THIRD PRISONER
          No one.

                    DEMON GUARD
          Who are you?

                    FOURTH PRISONER
          No one.

                    DEMON GUARD
          Who are you?

                    BUFFY
          I'm Buffy. The vampire slayer. And
          you are...?

The Demon guard swings his club. Buffy steps in, grabs his
arm, breaks it at the elbow, grabs the club and continues its
arc to hit the demon right in the chin. He flies back,
unconscious.

The other two guards rush her. The first she bludgeons
without looking at him as the second gets a heel to the face
followed by knuckles to the throat.

                                                    CONTINUED

32 CONTINUED: (2)   32

It's all over in a matter of seconds. Everyone looks at her,
stunned.

She turns to the others.

                    BUFFY (cont'd)
          Anyone who's not having fun here,
          follow me.

She heads out of the area, club in hand. A moment, and the
others follow.

33 INT. MAIN CHAMBER - MOMENTS LATER (NIGHT)   33

Buffy and the others arrive at the lower corner, stick to the
shadows. They look up to see:

ANGLE: THEIR POV

Across the chamber and all the way up is the ledge they'd
been standing on before. TWO GUARDS stand at it, looking
down.

                    BUFFY
          There's no way we can get there
          without meeting new people. Okay,
          Lily, when those guards leave, and
          they will, you take these guys and
          get up there. Fast and quiet.
          Anyone else wants to come along,
          fine, but you don't stop for
          anything. Clear?

                    LILY
          You're leaving me? But...

                    BUFFY
          Lily. You can handle this. 'Cause
          I say so.

They hear voices, see the shadows of guards approaching at a
run down the corridor.

                    BUFFY (cont'd)
          Ooh, we've gone public. Get them
          out. Go!

Lily starts out, then comes back.

                    LILY
          I'm sorry I said this was your fault
          before.
                                              CONTINUED

33 CONTINUED: 33

                              BUFFY
                    This can wait!

                              LILY
                    Well -- in case we die --

                              BUFFY
                    GO!

Lily takes off with the group. The guards appear and Buffy
runs into the main chamber with them on her heels.

                              BUFFY (cont'd)
                    Not yet, not yet...

She reaches the middle of the chamber --

                              BUFFY (cont'd)
                    Here's good.

Never slowing, she grabs a standing pole and swings around it
to plant her feet on the first guard's face. She drops and
takes out the other one just as quickly, arming herself with
a new cudgel and a twisted blade.

ANGLE: GUARDS

Turn as a siren sounds. They look about them to see what the
trouble is.

CRANE DOWN ON: BUFFY

Looking sweaty and cool as searchlights sweep across her
face. She's waiting for the fun.

"The fun" comes in the form of, say, FOUR DEMON GUARDS
rushing her. The first gets a hammer in the face, as Buffy
spins and hurls her blade in Braveheartian fashion into the
chest of the second. The rest of the fun will depend on the
dictates of the location, the time at hand, and a certain
amount of input from one of the 100 most creative people in
Hollywood. (Not Seth, the other one). Anyway, it's mean,
it's violent, it's good family viewing.

ANGLE: LILY AND THE GROUP

As they use Buffy's fight to make their move. They are
progressing through the shadows when a demon guard comes upon
them, taking out one with his cudgel. Lily and the rest
keep going.

ANGLE: KEN

                                                          CONTINUED

33 CONTINUED: (2)   33

A guard beside him, he looks out at the fight, rage filling
him.

                         KEN
              Humans don't fight back. **Humans
              don't fight back!** **THAT'S HOW THIS
              WORKS!!**

ANGLE: BUFFY

Proving him wrong.

                         KEN (cont'd)
                      (to the guard)
                   Get down there!

The guard dispatches himself Buffyward. Ken watches her a
moment, then stops, thinking. Takes off in another direction.

ANGLE: A COUPLE OF PRISONERS

Drift from their posts as their guards are occupied.

ANGLE: BUFFY

She moves to a new place, a couple of guards following, a
couple peeling off as they see prisoners leaving.

Buffy spars. She looks up as

ANGLE: A DEMON

dives at her from above, arms out, roaring with anger.

Buffy takes one step backward and the demon passes right
through frame, landing with a resolute THUD.

                         BUFFY
                   Demons: not that bright.

34 INT. SOME HALLWAY - NIGHT   34

As Lily leads the prisoners up toward the exit. She turns a
corner and Ken grabs her, holds a wicked looking knife to her
throat.

Without a word, he drags her off.

35 INT. MAIN CHAMBER - NIGHT   35   *

Buffy is getting worn down a bit when she hears: *

                                              CONTINUED

35 CONTINUED: 35

                         KEN
            One of you fights... and you all die!

She and the guards look up to see:

ANGLE: ON THE LEDGE BUFFY FIRST CAME OUT ON

Ken holds the blade to Lily.

Buffy stops. A couple of guards grab her.

Ken shoves Lily roughly aside, focussed on Buffy. He points
the knife at her, furious but calm.

                         KEN (cont'd)
            That... was not permitted.

                         BUFFY
            Yeah, but it was fun...

                         KEN
            You've got guts. I think I'd like to
            split you open and play with them.
                    (to the assembled)
            Let everyone know, this is the price
            of rebell --

Lily meekly shoves him off the ledge.

                         KEN (cont'd)
            --llioOOAA**AHHHHGHSCHRRGH!!**

He falls a long way and splats. Buffy laughs with surprise.

She knocks out the two guards holding her and heads on up.
(This may involve a spectacular stunt where she grabs a chain
that's going up and swings and dives and all kinds of
excitement. Or it may involve stairs.)

She disappears from the chamber.

36 INT. DIMENSIONAL PORTAL CHAMBER - CONTINUOUS - NIGHT   36

There is a portcullis of sorts cutting off access to the
mystical upside-down lap pool of freedom. About six people
are gathered in front of it. Buffy and Lily join them.

                         LILY
            They'll be coming.

                         BUFFY
            Hold on...

                                                    CONTINUED

                            50

36 CONTINUED: 36

She squats down, back to the gate, and grabs hold of it.
Starts straining to lift it. It's hard, but she starts
succeeding.

                    BUFFY (cont'd)
               Okay... this works the quads, and
               also the glutials...

As soon as there is a room, people start sliding under and
heading for the gate.

ANGLE: THE PORTAL

As people hoist each other through. Lily is the last to go
through, as Buffy lifts it high enough to let herself under
as well.

                    BUFFY (cont'd)
               Man, I'm gonna feel this for --

Ken slams into her, his face a mask of blood-soaked rage.
Buffy goes flying as the portcullis slams down impaling Ken's   *
legs.   *

He ends up on his knees, looking at Buffy who picks up a   *
cudgel and approaches him, a cold smile on her lips.*

                    KEN
               You... ruined... you...

                    BUFFY
               Hey Ken. Wanna see my impression of
               Gandhi?

Ken looks blearily at her. She swings the club down on his
head with horrible force. We hear a wet sound that comes
from inside his head.

Lily comes up to her, wide eyes on the corpse of Ken.

                    LILY
                 (weakly)
               Gandhi?

                    BUFFY
               Well, you know... if he was really
               pissed off.

37

    INT. CLEANSING CHAMBER - A FEW MOMENTS LATER (NIGHT)   37

Lily is out, helping Buffy out as well. Most of the others
have left or are leaving. Lily looks back at the pool.
                                          CONTINUED

37 CONTINUED: 37

                          LILY
                What do we do about --

ANGLE: THE POOL

As it flashes, the liquid disapearing, replaced by solid
stone.

Buffy kneels by it, touches it.

                          BUFFY
                It's closed. It's gone.

A moment more, and she stands, still looking down at the
stone.

38 INT. BUFFY'S APARTMENT - MORNING (DAY)   38

Buffy is showing Lily around the place.

                          BUFFY
                Let me give you the tour.

They turn to the right.

                          BUFFY (cont'd)
                This concludes our tour.

                          LILY
                It's really nice.

                          BUFFY
                The bathroom works a good part of the
                time. Don't bother to flip the
                mattress 'cause it doesn't get any
                better.

                          LILY
                I never had a place, you know, that
                I wasn't sharing.

                          BUFFY
                Well, it's paid up through the next
                three weeks.

She pulls her waitress outfit out of the closet, throws it on
the bed.

                          BUFFY (cont'd)
                I talked to Mitch at the diner and he
                said you could start on Thursday.
                          (more)

                                                          CONTINUED

38 CONTINUED: 38

                         BUFFY (cont'd)
               He's kind of, well, repulsive... but
               he won't give you a hard time. I'll
               be checking up on you, see how you're   *
               doing.   *

Lily sits on the bed, picks up the outfit. Pensive, a little
worried.

                         LILY
               I'm not great at taking care of
               myself.

                         BUFFY
               It gets easier. Takes practice.

Lily's eyes light up a bit.

                         LILY
               Hey...

She holds up Buffy's name tag...

                         LILY (cont'd)
               Can I be Anne?

Buffy smiles at her. Lily looks at the dress.   *

                         LILY (cont'd)   *
               I don't think I'll fit in this.   *

                         BUFFY   *
               You could wear it as a hat...   *

39 INT. BUFFY'S HOUSE - AFTERNOON (DAY)   39

Joyce is in the kitched, putting away some freshly washed   *
pots in a low drawer. The doorbell rings. She pops up,
anxious, then catches herself. Shakes her head.

She walks toward the door, wiping her hands with a dishtowel.
Something makes her pause, some instinct. She tosses the
towel on the table, moves more slowly to the foyer. To the
door.

Hand on the knob. Door swinging open. A beat.

She folds her daughter into her arms, and neither or them
moves.   *
                                          BLACK OUT.
               THE END   *

BUFFY THE VAMPIRE SLAYER

"Dead Man's Party"

Written By

Marti Noxon

Directed By

James Whitmore Jr.

<u>SHOOTING DRAFT</u>

July 21, 1998   (WHITE)
July 27, 1998   (BLUE)
July 29, 1998   (PINK)

BUFFY THE VAMPIRE SLAYER

"Dead Man's Party"

CAST LIST

```
BUFFY SUMMERS....................... Sarah Michelle Gellar
XANDER HARRIS....................... Nicholas Brendon
RUPERT GILES........................ Anthony S. Head
WILLOW ROSENBERG.................... Alyson Hannigan
CORDELIA CHASE...................... Charisma Carpenter
ANGEL............................... David Boreanaz
OZ.................................. Seth Green

JOYCE...............................
PRINCIPAL SNYDER....................* Armin Shimerman
PAT.................................* Nancy Lenehan
DEVON...............................
JONATHAN............................* Danny Strong
*STONER.............................* Chris Garnant
YOUNG DOCTOR........................* Paul Morgan Stetler

DINGOES ATE MY BABY..................
```

BUFFY THE VAMPIRE SLAYER

"Dead Man's Party"

SET LIST

INTERIORS

BUFFY'S HOUSE
     BUFFY'S BEDROOM
     JOYCE'S BEDROOM
     KITCHEN
     HALLWAY LEADING TO KITCHEN
     BASEMENT
     BASEMENT STAIRS
     HALLWAY OUTSIDE BASEMENT DOOR
     FOYER
     DINING ROOM
     UPSTAIRS HALLWAY
     STAIRWAY
     CLOSET
     HALLWAY OUTSIDE CLOSET
SUNNYDALE HIGH SCHOOL
     PRINCIPAL SNYDER'S OFFICE
     HALLWAY
     LIBRARY
GILES' APARTMENT
     LIVING ROOM
     KITCHEN AREA
JOYCE'S CAR
GILES' CAR
HOSPITAL EMERGENCY ROOM
COFFEE HOUSE

EXTERIORS

STREET
ALLEY
GILES' APARTMENT
     COURTYARD
COFFEE HOUSE – SHOPPING DISTRICT
*SUNNYDALE HIGH SCHOOL – FOUNTAIN QUAD
BUFFY'S HOUSE
     BACKYARD
HIGHWAY
PARK PLAYGROUND

BUFFY THE VAMPIRE SLAYER

"Dead Man's Party"

TEASER

1   INT. BUFFY'S BEDROOM - NIGHT   1

Buffy, looking a little worn from her return journey home,
finishes unpacking her duffle. She puts the last of her
clothes away, then stops for a long beat as she contemplates
her room - in some ways so familiar, yet so strange after
months away. Finally, she grabs her coat - heads out.

2   INT. BUFFY'S HOUSE - JOYCE'S BEDROOM - NIGHT   2

Buffy enters - unseen by Joyce, who is hanging some exotic
African art from the gallery in her bedroom. Joyce taps a
nail in to her wall with a hammer-

                    BUFFY
          Mom-

Joyce jumps. Knocks a chunk of plaster out of the wall.

                    JOYCE
          Oh! Buffy...

                    BUFFY
          Sorry, I-

                    JOYCE
          No, no... Don't worry about it. I
          guess I just got used to all the
          quiet while you were gone.
                    (then)
          But it's no problem. Look-

Joyce lifts a particularly mean-looking MASK from her dresser
and places it on the wall, covering the hole.

                    JOYCE (cont'd)
          Do you like it?

                    BUFFY
                    (trying)
          It's, um, really... I think I'd go
          with the hole.

CONTINUED

2 CONTINUED: 2

                         JOYCE
              It's from Nigeria. We got a very
              exciting shipment at the gallery. I
              thought I'd hang a few pieces in
              here. It cheers up the room.

                         BUFFY
              It's angry at the room. It wants the
              room to suffer.

                         JOYCE
              You have no appreciation of primitive
              art --

Now Joyce notices that Buffy is holding her coat. Works at
sounding casual - but the fun just left the building.

                         JOYCE (cont'd)
              Oh. You're...going out?

                         BUFFY
              If... if it's okay. I want to find
              Willow and Xander.

                         JOYCE
                    (worried)
              And - will you be slaying?

                         BUFFY
              Not unless they give me lip.

                         JOYCE
              Do you want a sandwich or something
              before you go? You must be starving.

                         BUFFY
              I was until that four course snack
              you served me after dinner...

                         JOYCE
              Well then - let me drive you. I
              mean, they could be anywhere-

                         BUFFY
              Mom, if you don't want me to go...

                         JOYCE
              No. I want to put this whole thing
              behind us. Get back to normal.
                    (then)
              You go - have a good time.

                                                    CONTINUED

2   CONTINUED: (2)   2

Buffy nods - exits. Joyce looks after her, uneasy. Turns
back to her task. Then Buffy pokes her head in again.

                         BUFFY
               Thanks.

WHAP. Joyce jumps and her hammer sinks into the wall again.

3   EXT. STREET - NIGHT   3

BUFFY walks along a quiet street, alert. Things don't feel
quite right. Then a LOUD NOISE - like someone knocking over
a trash can - comes from a nearby ally. Buffy immediately
kicks into full slayer mode. Follows the trail into the-

4   EXT. ALLEY - NIGHT   4

-where a MENACING FIGURE moves stealthily in the darkness.
Buffy approaches. Then she kicks a SODA CAN by accident -
sending it skittering noisily across the alley floor.

The FIGURE SPINS, startled. Now we can see that it's
XANDER - and he has a STAKE HEADED RIGHT FOR BUFFY'S HEART.

                                        BLACK OUT.

                    END OF TEASER

                                                    CONTINUED

ACT ONE

5   EXT. ALLEY - NIGHT   5

Back to that stake. Buffy manages to STOP IT with her hands,
just before it plunges into her chest. A beat - then she
smiles at Xander, unable to contain how glad she is to see
him.

                    BUFFY
          Didn't anyone tell you about playing
          with pointy sticks? It's all fun and
          games until someone loses an eye.

A stunned Xander takes in what just happened. And WHO it
just happened with.

                    XANDER
          You... shouldn't sneak up on people
          like that.

Another moment. Xander loses the cool, shakes his head.

                    XANDER (cont'd)
          Jeez, Buffy-

He opens his arms and they move to HUG EACH OTHER. It's
about to be a nice moment, but suddenly A PISSED OFF VAMPIRE
TACKLES XANDER.

Xander wrestles with the vamp, almost has the upper hand...
Then BUFFY BLINDSIDES THE VAMP and knocks him off Xander.

While the vamp tries to recover, BUFFY DRAWS A STAKE. Xander
leaps to his feet - also with STAKE DRAWN.

The VAMP GROWLS, starts to get up. BOTH Xander and Buffy
move to take him. They glance at each other.

                    BUFFY
          Oh. Go ahead.

                    XANDER
          No, you go.

                    BUFFY
          No, it's-

Now they are interrupted by a SHRILL ELECTRONIC SQUAWK
followed by-

                                                    CONTINUED

5 CONTINUED: 5

                    CORDELIA (O.C.)   *
          "Come in, Nighthawk. Everything
          okay?"

Buffy looks down and sees A FISHER PRICE STYLE WALKIE TALKIE
affixed to Xander's belt. She glances back at him - dubious.

                    BUFFY
          Nighthawk?

Embarassed, Xander fumbles for the walkie. The VAMP takes
advantage of their distraction and RUSHES THEM - this time
plowing into BUFFY.

CLOSE ON BUFFY AND THE VAMP

Struggling - as FOOTSTEPS sound the arrival of THREE MORE
PEOPLE. The VAMP IS YANKED off her.

REVEAL WILLOW AND CORDY

Who each have the VAMP by an ARM as they SLAM him into an
ALLEY WALL. The vamp thrashes madly.

                    CORDELIA
                  (struggling)
          Hello? This would be dust time!

Now the VAMP tosses them off. Willow hits the ground hard
while Cordelia falls into Buffy - who is back on her feet.
stake raised.

                    CORDELIA (cont'd)
                  (mild surprise)
          Oh. Buffy. Hey-

Buffy SHOVES CORDELIA out of the way of the vamp - who is now
behind Cordy, teeth bared. Without further ado, Buffy stakes
the guy and HE'S TOAST.

Buffy turns - faces WILLOW, OZ, CORDELIA and XANDER. We can
now fully register that they are all dressed for VAMP
HUNTING. In addition to slightly MILITARISITC outfits - they
wear CROSSES, make-shift STAKE HOLDERS and those colorful
WALKIE TALKIES.

A LONG BEAT - as everyone contemplates the suddenly returned
Buffy. Finally, an emotional Buffy manages-

                    BUFFY
          Hey.

                                                      CONTINUED

                              61

5   CONTINUED: (2)   5

At last the gang reacts, shocked and excited. Move in to
greet her.

6   EXT. GILES' APARTMENT - COURTYARD - NIGHT   6   *

Everyone gathers around Giles' door. Buffy, looking anious,   *
moves to knock - but stops.   *

                    BUFFY
          Are you sure it's not too late?   *
          Maybe we should come back tomorrow.   *

Everyone just looks at her - not buying it. Buffy goes to   *
knock again. Stops again.   *

                    BUFFY (cont'd)   *
          What if he's mad?

                    XANDER
          Mad? 'Cause you ran away and
          abandoned your post and your friends
          and your mother and made him lie
          awake every night worrying about you?
                    (to the others)   *
          Maybe we should wait out here.   *

7   OMITTED   7   *

Buffy gives Xander a look - takes a big breath - and finally   *
raps on the door.   *

A beat. Then Giles opens the door. Sees her. He's clearly
taken aback. Nobody says anything. Xander can't stand it.

                    XANDER
          Check it out. The watcher is back on
          the clock. And just when you were
          thinking career change. Maybe
          becoming a "Looker" or a "Seer"--

Giles cuts Xander off.

                    GILES
          Thank you, Xander.

Giles turns to Buffy - his expression closed, impossible to
read. Finally, his features soften and he addresses her -
trying to keep his composure.

                    GILES (cont'd)
          Welcome home, Buffy.

8   INT. GILES' APARTMENT - LIVING ROOM - NIGHT   8

Buffy, Giles, Willow, Oz, Xander and Cordelia all sit in the
living room.   They are in mid-conversation.

                    BUFFY
          ...Yeah, I just got in a few hours
          ago. Went to see Mom first...

                    GILES
          Of course. And how did you find her?

                    BUFFY
          I pretty much remembered the address.

                    GILES
          I mean, was everything all right
          between you --

He's cut off by the sound of A KETTLE BOILING.

                    GILES (cont'd)
          Ah. Excuse me.

The gang talks amongst themselves, while we follow Giles into
the-

9   INT. GILES' APARTMENT - KITCHEN AREA - CONT. - NIGHT   9

Where he proceeds to finish making a pot of tea.

                    OZ (O.S.)
          By the way, you're not wanted for
          murder anymore.

                    BUFFY (O.S.)
          Oh, good. That was such a drag.

                    XANDER (O.S.)
          So where were you? Did you go to
          Belgium?

                    BUFFY (O.S.)
          Why would I go to Belgium?

                    XANDER (O.S.)
          I think the relevant question is "why
          wouldn't you?" Belgium!

Giles moves to get the sugar - stops when he hears BUFFY'S
LAUGHTER ring above the other voices.

                                        CONTINUED

9 CONTINUED: 9

                         BUFFY (O.S.)
                    I'm glad to see you haven't changed,
                    Xander...

CLOSE ON GILES

Hidden from the others by a cabinet, they do not see Giles'
mask fall for a moment. He fights tears, his relief is
palpable. But... he pulls it together. Puts his WASP face
back on as he moves back into the-

10 INT. GILES' APARTMENT - LIVING ROOM - CONTINUOUS - NIGHT   10

                         GILES
                    Right, then. Tea's on.

Cordy grabs a cookie from the tray. Turns to Buffy.

                         CORDELIA
                    Okay - were you, like, living in a
                    box or what?

                         BUFFY
                    It's... a long story.

                         XANDER
                    So leave out the heartwarming stuff
                    about kindly old people and saving
                    the farm and get right to the dirt-

                         GILES
                    Perhaps Buffy could use a little time
                    to adjust before we grill her on her
                    summer activities.

                         BUFFY
                    What he said.

                         XANDER
                    Fair enough. In fact - you can leave
                    the slaying to us while you settle
                    in - we got you covered.

                         BUFFY
                    I noticed. You guys seemed down with
                    the slayage. All tricked out with
                    the walkies and everything-

                         CORDELIA
                    Yeah, but our outfits suck. That
                    Rambo thing is so over. I'm thinking
                    sporty. Hilfiger, maybe.

                                                  CONTINUED

10 CONTINUED: 10

                    WILLOW
               (enthusiastic)
          Still - we're getting good. I mean,
          we dust, like, 9 out of 10!

                    OZ
          6 out of 10.

                    WILLOW
               (with equal
                enthusiasm)
          6 out of 10!

                    XANDER
          Whatever. We've been kicking a
          little undead boot.

                    BUFFY
          Thanks for the offer, but I kind of
          want to get back to my routine. You
          know - slaying, school, kid stuff...
          You guys up for hanging tomorrow?
          I'm jonesing for some brainless fun.

An awkward beat. Then-

                    XANDER
          I would - but I'm tied up.

He puts a hand on Cordy. She smiles.

                    CORDELIA
          You wish.

                    BUFFY
          What about you, Will?

                    WILLOW
          Tomorrow? I...

                    BUFFY
          Come on. Friends don't let friends
          browse alone.

Will glances at Oz - hesitates, then-

                    WILLOW
          Okay. I had some school stuff,
          but... I guess I can change my plans.

                                              CONTINUED

65

10   CONTINUED: (2)   10

                         GILES
          As for school, Buffy, you know you'll
          have to talk with Principal Snyder
          before-

                         BUFFY
          On it. Mom's making an appointment
          with his ugliness.

                         GILES
          It may be tough going. He's quite
          emphatic about a Buffy-free Sunnydale
          High.

                         BUFFY
                    (covering her worry)
          No problem. I'm bringing The
          Intimidator. One look at "Mom Face"
          and I know he'll break.

11   INT. PRINCIPAL SNYDER'S OFFICE - DAY   11

CLOSE ON JOYCE

Who, indeed, is sporting a stern and intimidating "Mom Face."
But her look falters as-

                         PRINCIPAL SNYDER (O.S.)
          Absolutely not. Under no
          circumstances.

REVEAL SNYDER

At his desk - completely delighted with himself. Buffy sits
next to Joyce looking unhappy, but not shocked by Snyder's
attitude.

                         JOYCE
          But... you can't keep her out of
          school. You don't have the right.

                         PRINCIPAL SNYDER
          I have not only the right but also a
          nearly physical sensation of pleasure
          at the thought of keeping her out of
          school. I'd describe myself as
          tingly.

                         JOYCE
          Buffy was cleared of all those
          charges.

                                                    CONTINUED

11 CONTINUED: 11

                    PRINCIPAL SNYDER
          Yes, and while she may live up to the
          not-a-murderer requirement for
          enrollment, she is a troublemaker,
          destructive to school property and
          the occasional student and her grade
          point average alone is...
                    (smiles, forgetting
                     himself)
          I'm sorry. Another tingle moment.

                    JOYCE
          I don't see how you can be so
          cavalier about a young girl's entire
          future.

                    PRINCIPAL SNYDER
          I'm quite sure a girl with talents
          and abilities such as Buffy's will
          land on her feet.
                    (glee returning)
          In fact, I noticed on the way in this
          morning that Hot Dog On A Stick is
          hiring.
                    (to Buffy)
          You'll look so cute in that hat.

     Buffy stands. Grabs her bag.

                    BUFFY
          Let's go, Mom.

                    JOYCE
          This isn't over. If I have to, I'll
          go all the way to the mayor.

                    PRINCIPAL SNYDER
          Wouldn't that be interesting.

     Smiling, he opens the door - showing them out.

12   INT. SCHOOL HALLWAY - DAY   12

     Joyce follows Buffy out into the hall. Giles, who's been
     lingering but trying not to look like he's been lingering,
     approaches.

                    GILES
          Well. How did it go?

                                                      CONTINUED

12 CONTINUED: 12

                          JOYCE
                        (furious)
              Have you ever noticed his teeth?
              They're like tiny, little rodent
              teeth-

                          GILES
              Oh, dear...

                          JOYCE
              Horrible gnashing little teeth. You
              just want to pull them out with
              pliers.

                          GILES
              Perhaps there's some way he can be
              over-ruled...

Now Joyce and Giles move away from Buffy, talking intently
about her "situation." The BELL RINGS and the hall is
suddenly flooded with students - all moving with purpose from
one class to the next.

CLOSE ON BUFFY

As the kids pass, not seeming to notice her. She looks, and
feels, lost - displaced.

13 INT. JOYCE'S CAR - DAY   13

Joyce pulls up to the curb with Buffy in the passenger seat.
Both look discouraged, but Joyce tries to sound cheery.

                          JOYCE
              Don't worry about school, honey. If
              we can't get you back into
              Sunnydale, we may be able to swing
              private school.

                          BUFFY
                        (horrified)
              Like with the jackets and kilts? You
              want me to get field-hockey-knees?

                          JOYCE
              It's not that bad.

                          BUFFY
              How about home schooling? It's not
              just for scary religious people
              anymore.

                                              CONTINUED

13 CONTINUED: 13

                    JOYCE
          We'll work something out.

Buffy just nods. Joyce gives her a quick peck on the cheek.

                    JOYCE (cont'd)
          Tell Willow I said hi.

14 EXT. COFFEE HOUSE - SHOPPING DISTRICT STREET - DAY   14

Buffy waits for Willow outside of a coffee house. It's clear
that she's been waiting for a while. She checks her watch...
She sits on a bench - decides to give it a few more minutes.

15 EXT. BUFFY'S HOUSE - FRONT DOOR - DAY   15

Buffy comes up the walk as the front door opens and an
unfamiliar women in her 40's steps out - PAT. She's of the
chatty, nervous variety.

                    PAT
          Oh my word, you must be Buffy! Look
          at you - aren't you a picture?

                    BUFFY
          Thanks...

                    PAT
              (shaking Buffy's hand
              enthusiastically)
          I'm Pat - from your mother's book
          club? I'm sure she mentioned me.

                    BUFFY
          Actually-

                    PAT
          I sort of took it upon myself to look
          after her while you were, you know,
          off and away or what have you.
          Between your "situation" and reading
          "Deep End of the Ocean" she was just
          a wreck. You can imagine.

Buffy might reply but Pat is already heading for the street.

                    PAT (CONT'D)
          Well, I'm off. We're making
          empanadas in my Spanish class
          tonight. You go be with your mother.
          The two of you need to re-bond.

                                              CONTINUED

15 CONTINUED: 15

Pat hustles away - leaving Buffy a little dazed.

16 INT. BUFFY'S HOUSE - KITCHEN - DAY   16

Joyce is looking through a cook book when Buffy enters,
looking irritated.

> BUFFY
> Pat wishes us quality time.

> JOYCE
> Oh - I met her in-

> BUFFY
> Book Club. Got it.

> JOYCE
> Before I forget - Willow just called.

> BUFFY
> Where was she?

> JOYCE
> She got held up. But she said she
> tried to call.

> BUFFY
> Was there a message?

Again, Joyce tries to put a happy face on things - but the
strain is growing more forced.

> JOYCE
> No... But I had a thought - what if
> I invited Willow and Mr. Giles and
> everyone for dinner tomorrow night?
> Don't you think that would be nice?

Buffy's clearly not sure - but...

> JOYCE (cont'd)
>   (sheepishly)
> Since I sort of already did, I'm
> hoping for a yes.

> BUFFY
> It'll be fun.

> JOYCE
> Why don't you run downstairs and get
> the company plates.

CONTINUED

16   CONTINUED: 16

                              BUFFY
                    Mom. Willow and everybody aren't
                    company plate people. They're normal
                    plate people.

                              JOYCE
                    We never have guests for dinner.
                    Indulge your mother.

        She gives Buffy "Mom Face." Buffy starts to move - then
        stops.

                              BUFFY
                    So how come that face works on me - but
                    not on other people?

                              JOYCE
                    It's genetic.

        Buffy nods - goes into the basement.

17   INT. BUFFY'S HOUSE - BASEMENT - DAY   17

        Buffy enters, gets the china from a shelf and notices a stack
        of framed photos nearby. She turns one over.

        CLOSE ON THE PHOTO

        It's a picture of BUFFY, WILLOW & XANDER from a year or so
        back. They are arm in arm, laughing.

        ON BUFFY

        As she regards it for a long beat - feeling like she's
        looking at a picture from someone else's life. She move to
        put it back on the shelf, but in doing so dislodges AN OBJECT
        which nearly falls on her head.

        When it lands on the floor we see that it's a DEAD CAT, stiff
        with RIGOR MORTIS. Buffy shrieks with surprise, jumps.

18   EXT. BACKYARD - DAY   18

        The sun is setting as Buffy DIGS A HOLE in a flower bed. She
        puts her spade aside and Joyce drops the cat (now in a
        plastic hefty bag) into the hole.

                              BUFFY
                    Next time? I get to pick the
                    mother/daughter bonding activity...

                                                          CONTINUED

18 CONTINUED: 18

A sad beat as they contemplate the grave.

                    JOYCE
          You want to - say something?

                    BUFFY
          What? Thanks for stopping by and
          dying?

                    JOYCE
          How about - goodbye stray cat, who
          lost it's way. We hope... you find
          it.

Joyce's last comment resonates a bit too much for both of
them. Buffy starts to shovel the dirt back into the grave.

19 INT. BUFFY'S BEDROOM - NIGHT   19

Buffy gets into bed and turns out the light - but she just
lies there with her eyes open. She looks toward the window
and the night shadows playing on the wall. It all looks
unfamiliar, cold.

20 INT. JOYCE'S BEDROOM - NIGHT   20

Joyce is asleep and unaware of THE MASK on her wall as IT'S
EYES START TO GLOW.

21 EXT. BACKYARD - NIGHT   21   *

The ground where the stray cat lies buried MOVES. Then a PAW
emerges from the dirt and the CAT CRAWLS AND SCRATCHES ITS
WAY OUT OF THE GRAVE - A ZOMBIE PET.

22 INT. JOYCE'S BEDROOM - NIGHT   22

Now the eyes in the mask BURN RED.

23 EXT. BACKYARD - NIGHT   23

The zombie cat straggles across the yard and stops under
JOYCE'S BEDROOM WINDOW.

                                                    CONTINUED

23 CONTINUED: 23

It looks up toward the window and MEOWS in a discordant,
otherworldy tone.

                                                BLACK OUT.

                    END OF ACT ONE

                                                CONTINUED

ACT TWO

24   INT. SCHOOL HALLWAY - DAY   24

The hallway stands empty, except for BUFFY, who wanders a bit
aimlessly. Doors stand open, revealing deserted classrooms.

25   EXT. SCHOOL - FOUNTAIN QUAD - DAY   25   *

Now Buffy is outside. Again, she's alone. The school is
desolate. A ghost town.

Then someone moves to her side. Angel.

                    BUFFY
          I thought they would be here.

                    ANGEL
          They are. They're waiting for you.

                    BUFFY
          Am I dreaming?

                    ANGEL
                (smiles)
          I'm probably the wrong person to ask.
          You'd better go.

                    BUFFY
          I'm afraid.

                    ANGEL
                (matter-of-factly)
          You should be.

     AND A SCHOOL BELL RINGS.

26   INT. BUFFY'S BEDROOM - DAY   26

Buffy's ALARM is sounding. She wakes from her dream.

27   INT. BUFFY'S HOUSE - KITCHEN - DAY   27

Joyce is pouring herself some coffee as Buffy looks in the
fridge. The tension between them is not quite "cut with a
knife" thick - but it's getting there.

                                             CONTINUED

27 CONTINUED: 27

                    JOYCE
          I've been on the phone with the
          superintendent of schools. He seems
          more reasonable than that nasty
          little horrid bigoted rodent man.

She says it offhand, as though it were Snyder's full name.

                    BUFFY
          Mom-

                    JOYCE
          -anyway, I'm going in to speak with
          him this afternoon. As for private
          schools-
                    (she pushes some
                    papers toward Buffy)
          Miss Porter's accepts late
          admissions. I wrote down the
          information for you-

                    BUFFY
          A girl's school? Okay - so now it's
          jackets, kilts, and no boys? Care to
          throw in a little foot binding?

                    JOYCE
                    (hard)
          Buffy. You made some bad choices.
          You may just have to live with some
          consequences.

Buffy reacts to Joyce's tone. Joyce immediately relents.

                    JOYCE (cont'd)
          Nothing's settled yet. I just wish
          you didn't have to be so secretive
          about things. I mean, it's not your
          fault you have a special
          circumstance. They should make
          allowances for you.

                    BUFFY
          Mom. Please. I'm a slayer. It's
          not like I have to ride the little
          bus to school.

Joyce carries some trash to the kitchen door, opens it.   *
Still, she pauses to finish her thought.   *

                    JOYCE
          Couldn't you just tell a few people?   *
          Like Principal Snyder?

                                              CONTINUED

27   CONTINUED: (2)   27   *
                                                                                       *

                              JOYCE (cont'd)
                    And maybe the police? I'm sure
                    they'd be happy to know that they
                    have a superhero -- is that the right
                    term? It's not offensi -- AAAAHGH!

Joyce and Buffy react to the ZOMBIE CAT - who ZIPS through
the open door and into the house.

28   INT. BUFFY'S HOUSE - FOYER - DAY   28

A grim looking Buffy opens the door for GILES, who carries a
small animal cage.

                              BUFFY
                    Welcome to the Hellmouth petting zoo.

29   INT. JOYCE'S BEDROOM - DAY   29

ON THE ZOMBIE CAT

Who SCREECHES HORRIBLY as Giles catches it. He HOLDS THE
CREATURE FAR AWAY from his body as he deposits it in the
cage, reacting visibly to its BAD SMELL.

                              GILES
                    My lord - what a stench.

                              BUFFY
                    I told mom, get the Forest Pine or
                    the April Fresh - but she wanted dead
                    cat.

Giles looks to Joyce, who stands nearby - freaked. On top of
the obvious weirdness - there's also still tension between
them after their last talk.

                              GILES
                    I'll take it back to the library and
                    we'll try to determine its exact
                    origin.

As he's leaving, Giles notices the MASK among the artifacts
on Joyce's wall. Tries to make nice with her.

                              GILES (cont'd)
                    This is striking. Nigerian?

                                                          CONTINUED

29 CONTINUED: 29

                         JOYCE
              Yes, I have this wonderful dealer who
              specializes in ancient-

They'd go on but Buffy jumps in, eager for some distraction.

                         BUFFY
              You know I love art talk as much as
              the next very dull person - but
              Giles, shouldn't we go? We're in
              research mode.

She starts for the door, but Giles hesitates.

                         GILES
              You ought to stay here with your
              mother, Buffy. I'm sure you have
              lots of-

                         JOYCE
                    (interrupting)
              Please. It's fine. She can go with
              you.

                         GILES
              Actually, she can't.
                    (to Buffy)
              You're not allowed on school property.

                         BUFFY
              Oh.
                    (embarassed)
              This marks a first. I want to go to
              school - but school doesn't want me.

                         GILES
              I'm sorry. I'll call as soon as I
              know something.

                         JOYCE
              And we'll see you tonight. Dinner?

                         GILES
              Ah - of course. Tonight, then.

And he goes, leaving Buffy feeling even more the outcast.

30 INT. LIBRARY - DAY   30

ON ZOMBIE CAT

Who is pacing, restless, in his cage.

                                                   CONTINUED

30   CONTINUED: 30

WIDEN TO INCLUDE CORDELIA AND OZ

Who are close to the cage - checking it out. The cat HISSES
at them in its strange cadence.

                    OZ
          Looks dead. Smells dead. But moving
          around. Interesting.

Cordelia moves away from the creature, disgusted.

                    CORDELIA
          Nice pet, Giles. Don't you like
          anything regular? Golf or USA Today
          or anything?

Now we see that GILES, WILLOW and XANDER are all hitting the
books. Looking up "reanimation" and stuff like that.

                    GILES
          We're trying to find how and why it
          rose from the grave. It's not as if
          I'm going to take it home and serve
          it a warm saucer of milk-

                    OZ
          I like him. I think you should call
          him Patches.

                    WILLOW
          Hey - what about Buffy's Welcome home
          dinner tonight? I told her mom we'd
          help out. Bring stuff.

                    CORDELIA
          I'm the dip!

Everybody looks at her. Xander beams.

                    XANDER
          You have to admire the purity of it.

                    CORDELIA
          What? Onion dip. Stirring. Not
          cooking. That's what I bring.

                    OZ
          Well - let's figure it out. What
          kind of deal is this. Is it a
          gathering, a shin dig or a hootenanny?

                    CORDELIA
          What's the difference?

                                                    CONTINUED

78

30 CONTINUED: (2)   30

                         OZ
             A gathering. Brie and mellow song
             stylings. Shin dig. Dip-
                      (he nods to Cordelia)
             Less mellow song stylings. Perhaps
             a large amount of malt beverage. And
             a hootenanny... just chock full of
             hoot and a little bit of nanny.

                         XANDER
             I hate brie.

                         CORDELIA
             I know. It smells like Giles' cat.

Giles starts to protest.

                         GILES
             It's not my-

                         XANDER
             And what would we talk about at a
             "gathering" anyway? "So Buffy - run
             into any nice pimps on your travels?
             And by the by, thanks for ruining our
             lives for the past three months..."

                         WILLOW
             Xander-

                         XANDER
             You know what I mean. She doesn't
             want to talk about it. We don't want
             talk about it. Maybe we should
             shut up and dance.

                         WILLOW
             Buffy did say she wanted to loosen
             up. Have some kid time.
                      (to Oz)
             Hey. Aren't you guys rehearsing
             tonight? Why don't you play at the
             party.

                         OZ
             Yeah. I think I could supply some
             Dingo action.

Giles looks up from his studies, a little concerned.

                         GILES
             I'm not sure that a... shin dig-

                                                         CONTINUED

30 CONTINUED: (3)   30

Oz politely stops him.

                    OZ
          Hootenanny.

                    GILES
          Hootenanny... is the best order of the
          day. Maybe it's best to keep things
          more intimate. Buffy just got
          home - I'm sure she's still feeling
          disoriented.

                    WILLOW
          All the more reason to make her feel
          welcome. And a big party says,
          Welcome, Buffy!

                    XANDER
          Okay - so one vote from the old guy
          for smelly cheese night - and, how
          many votes for actual fun?

Everybody else's hand goes up. They all look at Giles.

                    GILES
          Very well. Have it your way. I'm
          just glad to have her home...

CLOSE ON GILES' BOOK

As, distracted, he turns PAST a picture of THE MASK that
hangs on JOYCE'S WALL.

                    GILES (O.C.)
          Now things can get back to normal.

                                                    DISSOLVE TO:

31 INT. JOYCE'S BEDROOM - NIGHT   31

PUSH IN ON THE MASK ITSELF

As the EYES START TO GLOW

32 EXT. HIGHWAY - NIGHT   32

As A CORONER'S AIDE outlines a BODY at a crime scene with a
piece of chalk. TWO POLICE CARS, lights flashing, separate
the aide from the COPS and EMERGENCY WORKERS who bustle in
the background.

                                                    CONTINUED

32 CONTINUED: 32

Suddenly, the CORPSE AWAKENS. It grabs the aide by the
throat, silencing his cries. Now the zombie DRAGS THE
FLAILING AIDE into some bushes - unnoticed by the others on
the scene. The piece of chalk trails on the pavement,
drawing a line as he goes...

33 INT. BUFFY'S HOUSE - DINING ROOM - NIGHT   33

Buffy is setting the table when the DOORBELL RINGS. She goes
to the door, expecting her buddies - but instead is
confronted by her mother's friend PAT.

                    PAT
          There you are. Not thinking about
          any more flights of fancy, I hope?
                    (not giving Buffy a
                    chance to reply)
          Joyce said there was room for one
          more - so I said "forget facial
          night - let's Party!" I bet you like
          empanadas.

She thrusts a tupperware container into Buffy's hands. Now
they just stand there - uncomfortable. Finally-

                    BUFFY
          You want to see my mother?

                    PAT
          Please.

                    BUFFY
          MOM!

Joyce comes down the stairs, just finishing dressing - sees
Pat.

                    JOYCE
          Oh, Pat. Good. Buffy, I hope you
          don't mind-

But she's interrupted as the DOORBELL RINGS AGAIN. Buffy
answers it and is more than a little surprised to see DEVON
from the band and a bunch of GROUPIE TYPES.

                    DEVON
          Hey, Buffy.

                    BUFFY
          Uh, hey.

                                                    CONTINUED

33 CONTINUED: 33

                         DEVON
               So - where do you want the band to
               set up?

                         BUFFY
                    (stunned)
               The band?

                                                        CUT TO:

34 INT. BUFFY'S HOUSE - LIVING ROOM - NIGHT   34

DINGOES ATE MY BABY jam in the living room. There are too
many people - most of whom Buffy doesn't even know - crammed
into the room. It's a weird vibe.

Buffy wanders, not knowing what to do with herself. She
spots WILLOW across the room watching OZ play. Buffy moves
to her and they yell over the band.

                         BUFFY
               Hey!

                         WILLOW
               Hey!

                         BUFFY
               This is... large!

                         WILLOW
               You like?

                         BUFFY
               It's great. It's just - I was
               thinking more, just us. The gang?

Willow shakes her head. Can't hear Buffy over the music.

                         WILLOW
               Sorry - what!?

                         BUFFY
               This is amazing. But I still want to
               hang with just-

Willow smiles - but mouths the words "I Can't Hear You."
Turns back to the band.

Buffy starts to move away - but changes her mind and pulls
Willow aside, where they can hear one another.

                                                        CONTINUED

34 CONTINUED: 34

                         BUFFY (cont'd)
                Is everything okay? You seem to
                be... I don't know - avoiding me.
                In the one-on-one sense.

Willow smiles - but she's clearly uncomfortable.

                         WILLOW
                What? This isn't avoiding. See?
                Here you are. Here I am.

                         BUFFY
                So - we're cool?

                         WILLOW
                Way. That's why - with the party.
                'Cause we're all glad you're back.

A beat. Buffy nods. But she sounds uncertain...

                         BUFFY
                Okay.

                         WILLOW
                Okay. Good.

And Willow moves back toward the band. Buffy watches her -
wondering why she doesn't feel any better.

35 INT. JOYCE'S ROOM - NIGHT   35

The eyes of the MASK glow.

36 INT. HOSPITAL - EMERGENCY ROOM - NIGHT   36

A guy lies DEAD on the table, a victim of a horrible burn.
Flat-line city. A YOUNG DOCTOR does CPR on him. An INTERN
and a NURSE stand nearby.

The doctor stops his efforts. Checks his watch.   *

                         YOUNG DOCTOR
                It's 7:43. Let's call it. He's not   *
                coming back.

                                                          CONTINUED

36   CONTINUED: 36

Suddenly we see the ZOMBIE SIT UP ON THE TABLE and LUNGE for
the doctor.

As everyone rushes to pull the zombie off, we see the HEART
MONITOR. It's STILL SHOWING A FLAT LINE.

CLOSE ON MONITOR.

As, REFLECTED IN THE MONITOR, everyone screams and very bad
things ensue.

37   INT. BUFFY'S HOUSE - LIVING ROOM - NIGHT   37

The party is verging on WILD. People dance. The ubiquitous
JONATHAN chats up a CUTE GIRL, who looks like she'd rather be
anywhere else.

                    JONATHAN
          ...I think you'll be impressed. It's
          the Cadillac of mopeds...

That's it. The girl walks away. Jonathan plays it off like
it's all good. No problemo...

Now we see BUFFY moving among the guests - a stranger in a   *
strange land. She nods her head to the music - trying to   *
look cooler than she feels, passes two STONER TYPES who stand
surveying the crowd.

                    STONER   *
                 (to the other stoner   *
                  dude)   *
          This Party? I heard it's for some   *
          chick who just got our of rehab.

The other stoner just nods. Buffy overhears this - decides   *
to make herself scarce. Exits the living room.   *

38   INT. BUFFY'S HOUSE - FOYER - CONTINUOUS - NIGHT   38

Buffy turns a corner and runs right into XANDER and CORDELIA,
who are in heavy-petting mode.

She does an about-face, but Xander SEES her. He continues to
hold and caress Cordelia while he addresses Buffy.

                    XANDER
          Hey, Buffy. What you doing?

Buffy turns back - caught.

                                                         CONTINUED

38 CONTINUED: 38

                              BUFFY
                    Don't mind me. I was just - taking
                    a break from all that wacky fun.

                              XANDER
                    Some party, huh? Guess a lot of
                    people are glad you're back.

                              BUFFY
                    Yeah. Seems like people I don't even
                    know missed me.
                              (then)
                    Did Giles say if he was going to be
                    late?

                              XANDER
                    He was library man last time I saw
                    him. But he'll be here. He wants to
                    celebrate your homecoming. We all
                    do. I mean, it's great having the
                    Buffster back.
                              (to Cordy)
                    Isn't it?

                              CORDELIA
                    Totally.
                              (to Xander)
                    Except - you were kinda turning me on
                    with that whole "boy slayer" look.

                              XANDER
                    Was I now?

                              CORDELIA
                    You bet - "Nighthawk..."

She giggles. And that's it - they're lost in touch town
again.

                              BUFFY
                    Okay. So. I'll just...

Buffy - totally forgotten - backs away as they start to
nuzzle each other.

39 INT. BUFFY'S HOUSE - KITCHEN - NIGHT   39

Joyce is getting some more ice - stops when she sees A BOTTLE
BURIED IN A WALL OF ICE.

                              JOYCE
                    Ooohhh. Look what I found.

                                                            CONTINUED

39 CONTINUED: 39

Joyce YANKS on the bottle, finally ripping it free. She
turns to Pat, presenting her bounty - an ice encrusted bottle
of PEACH SCHNAPPS. Then she grabs a couple of glasses and
pours them each a shot.

                    JOYCE (cont'd)
               The kids have their fun - we have
               ours.

A beat as they sip the schnapps. Now Pat changes gears -
addressing Joyce in a maternal, concerned manner...

                    PAT
               Now - how are you holding up, Joyce?
               Really?

                    JOYCE
               Really? I'm...
                    (then/letting down)
               I don't know. While Buffy was
               gone - all I could think about was
               getting her home. I just knew if I
               could put my arms around her and tell
               her how much I loved her - then
               everything would be okay...

                    PAT
               But?

                    JOYCE
               But things are never that simple, are
               they? I mean, she's here. She's
               right in front of me... So now I can
               see how unhappy she is. And I still
               don't know what to say - what to
               do - to make things right.

40 INT. HALLWAY LEADING TO KITCHEN - CONTINUOUS - NIGHT   40

Buffy, still looking for a safe place to hang, moves toward
the kitchen. Stops when she overhears-

                    JOYCE (cont'd)
               Having Buffy home - I thought it
               would make it all better. But in
               some ways, it's almost worse...

CLOSE ON BUFFY

Who takes her mother's words like a slap. Retreats.

41   INT. BUFFY'S ROOM - NIGHT   41

      Buffy enters - reeling. A long beat. Then she grabs her
      duffle from her closet. Starts packing.

A42   EXT. PARK - PLAYGROUND - NIGHT   A42   *

      From the shadows emerges the ZOMBIE we saw on the highway and   *
      the ZOMBIE from the ER.   *

      Behind them more ZOMBIES arrive. A small army of them. Once   *
      gathered, they set course and lumber with purpose - RIGHT   *
      TOWARD US.

42   EXT. BUFFY'S HOUSE - NIGHT   42   *

      Where we can hear the party, the revelers within blissfully   *
      unaware of what's coming.   *

A43   INT. JOYCE'S BEDROOM - NIGHT   A43   *

      As the eyes of the mask GLOW BRIGHTER...   *

                                          BLACK OUT.

                          END OF ACT TWO

ACT THREE

43   INT. LIBRARY - NIGHT   43

Giles is reading another book about reanimation. He stops,
finding something troubling.

                         GILES
           Oh lord.

Now he grabs a book off his desk - rifles through it until he
FINDS THE PICTURE OF THE MASK that he missed earlier. He
reads anxiously - then goes to his phone. Dials. Waits
impatiently as it rings and rings.

                                        INTERCUT WITH:

44   INT. BUFFY'S HOUSE - FOYER - NIGHT   44

THE PHONE chimes, unnoticed, as music BLARES and the party
rages on.

Finally. one of the STONER DUES that Buffy overheard talking
earlier ambles by. He notices the phone. Picks it up.

                         STONER   *
           Party villa. Can I rock you?

                         GILES
           Excuse me? Hello?

                         STONER   *
           What can I do for you, London
           sounding guy?

                         GILES
           I need to speak with Buffy. Right
           away. I have some information here
           that's rather urgent -

Somebody breaks a glass somewhere. People cheer. The stoner *
cheers.   *

                         STONER   *
           YEAH! Fiesta foul! You gotta do a
           shot!

                         GILES
                (losing it)
           I need to speak to Buffy! Right now!

                                              CONTINUED

88

44   CONTINUED: 44   *

                         STONER   *
              Bunny?
                   (to his stoner bud,   *
                    concerned)   *
              That guy has to do a shot.

                         GILES
              BUFFY!

Stoner dude holds the phone out to no one in particular.

                         STONER   *
              Hey! Is there a BUDDY here! I need
              a Buddy...

A beat. Nobody pays any attention to him. He shrugs.

                         STONER (contd)   *
              Sorry. He's not here. You got the
              wrong casa, Mr. Belvedere.

And he HANGS UP ON GILES.

45   INT. LIBRARY - NIGHT   45

Now Giles is talking to a dial tone.

                         GILES
              Hell- Hello...?

Exasperated, he slams the phone down. A moment as he
considers his options. Then he grabs his coat and TAKES OFF.

46   INT. BUFFY'S HOUSE - UPSTAIRS HALLWAY - NIGHT   46

Willow comes up the stairs, heads toward the bathroom.
She notices that the door to Buffy's room is open a crack -
and sees Buffy moving around inside.

Willow stops - feeling remorseful about her earlier snub -
and moves to the door. Reacts when she sees that Buffy is
PACKING UP HER STUFF.

47   INT. BUFFY'S BEDROOM - NIGHT   47

Willow enters, unseen by Buffy.

                                                      CONTINUED

47   CONTINUED: 47

>   WILLOW
>   You're leaving again? What, you just
>   stopped by to pick up your lint brush
>   and now you're ready to go?

>   BUFFY
>   It's not like anyone'll mind.

>   WILLOW
>   Oh, no, go ahead. Have a great time,
>   don't forget to **not write**.

>   BUFFY
>   Why are you attacking me? I'm
>   trying --

>   WILLOW
>   Wow, and it looks so much like giving
>   up!

>   BUFFY
>   I'm just trying to make things easier.

>   WILLOW
>   For who?

>   BUFFY
>   You guys seemed to be doing fine
>   without me.

>   WILLOW
>   We did the best we could! We didn't
>   have much choice in the matter.

>   BUFFY
>   Look, I'm sorry I had to leave, okay?
>   You don't know what I was going
>   through.

>   WILLOW
>   What you were going through?
>   Buffy... what about me?

>   BUFFY
>   Willow, I know you were worried,
>   but --

>   WILLOW
>   No, I mean what about me? My life.
>   I have all sorts of -- I'm dating,
>   I'm having serious dating...
>   (more)

                                                        CONTINUED

47   CONTINUED: (2)   47

                         WILLOW (cont'd)
               with a werewolf, and I've been
               studying witchcraft and killing
               vampires, and you were my **best
               friend**, I didn't have anyone to talk
               to about all this scary life stuff.
               Then you come back and you didn't
               even ask about me. You just worried
               about whether I was mad at you.

OFF BUFFY

Stunned and shamed by Willow's words.

48   INT. GILES' CAR - NIGHT   48

Desperate to get to Buffy's, Giles SPEEDS down the street.

                         GILES
               Unbelieveable...
                    (as Joyce)
               "Do you like my mask? Isn't it
               pretty? It raises the dead!"
                    (himself)
               Americans...

A FIGURE steps into his path. There's no time to stop and he
HITS IT with a sickening THUD.

Giles stops the car - mortified.

49   EXT. STREET - NIGHT   49

Giles steps out of his car. The street is eerily quiet and
the person he hit LIES FACE DOWN AND COMPLETELY MOTIONLESS.

                         GILES
               Are you all right? Can you move?

Giles approaches and gently turns the body over. Reacts when
he sees that IT'S A HORRIBLY DECAYED CORPSE that has clearly
been dead for DAYS.

                         GILES (cont'd)
               Good God-

Then the corpse's EYES SNAP OPEN. Giles starts and pushes
away from the dead dude, only to see THREE MORE ZOMBIES
SLOWLY MOVE OUT OF THE SHADOWS - RIGHT TOWARD HIM.

The Zombie on the ground grabs him.

50   INT. BUFFY'S HOUSE - UPSTAIRS HALLWAY - NIGHT   50

Joyce comes up the stairs - picking up discarded cups and
napkins people have left on the floor. She stops when she
hears Buffy and Willow in heated conversation.

                    BUFFY (O.C.)
          ...how much I missed you, and
          everyone! I wanted to call every day-

                    WILLOW (O.C.)
          It doesn't matter, Buffy! It still
          doesn't make it okay that you-

Drawn by the sound of their argument - Joyce moves to Buffy's
room.

51   INT. BUFFY'S ROOM - CONTINUOUS - NIGHT   51

Joyce pushes the door open - sees the half-packed bag and
clothes littered around. Can't believe her eyes.

                    JOYCE
          This is a joke - right?

                    BUFFY
          Mom - can you just - Willow and I are
          talking-

                    JOYCE
          No - I can't "just!" What is this
          Buffy?

                    WILLOW
          She was running away again.

Buffy's getting overwhelmed.

                    BUFFY
          I - I wasn't. I mean, I'm not sure
          what-

                    JOYCE
               (interrupting her)
          Well you better get sure and explain
          yourself right away! Because if you
          think you can just take off any time
          you-

                    BUFFY
          Stop! Just - stop! I don't know.
          Okay? I don't know what I'm doing.

                                              CONTINUED

51   CONTINUED: 51

She pushes past her mother and OUT OF THE ROOM. Joyce is hot   *
on her heels.

52   INT. BUFFY'S HOUSE - FOYER - NIGHT   52

Buffy, trailed closely by Joyce, finds the front door BLOCKED
by XANDER and CORDY - still in make-out mode.

                    JOYCE
          Don't you leave this house, young
          lady!

Xander and Cordy react to Joyce - breaking their embrace and
turning toward Buffy. Not wanting to face them, Buffy
changes coordinates and moves into the-

53   INT. BUFFY'S HOUSE - LIVING ROOM - NIGHT   53

Where she barely makes it into the room before Joyce is on
her - grabbing her by the elbow.

                    JOYCE
          That's it! You and I are going to
          have a talk.

Buffy notices people react to her mother's obvious anger.

                    BUFFY
          Mom. Please-

But Joyce just gets louder.

                    JOYCE
          You know what? I don't care. I
          don't care what your friends think of
          me - or you for that matter - because
          you put me through the wringer,
          Buffy. I mean it. And I've had
          schnapps!

Willow comes into the room - moves to OZ. Also - Xander and
Cordy have entered to see what the commotion is about.

                    JOYCE (cont'd)
          Do you have any idea what it's been
          like?

                    BUFFY
          Mom-

                                                        CONTINUED

93

53   CONTINUED: 53

                        JOYCE
          You can't imagine. Months of not
          knowing. Not knowing if you were
          lying dead in a ditch somewhere or -
          I don't know - living it up-

That's it - Buffy really loses it.

                        BUFFY
          But you told me! You're the one who
          said I should go. You said - "if you
          leave this house, don't come back."
          You found out who I really am and you
          couldn't deal - remember?

CLOSE ON PARTY GUESTS

As they get more and more uncomfortable. People start to
back out of the room - slip out the front door.

BACK ON BUFFY, WILLOW, XANDER, CORDY AND OZ

                        JOYCE
               (aghast)
          Buffy! You didn't give me any time.
          You just dumped this... this thing on
          me and expected me to get it.
          Well - guess what? Mom's not
          perfect. I handled it badly. But
          that doesn't give you the right to
          punish me by running away-

                        BUFFY
          Punish you? I didn't do this to
          punish you-

                        XANDER
          Well you did. You should have seen
          what it did to her.

                        BUFFY
               (exasperated)
          Great. Would anybody else care to
          weigh in? What about you? By the
          dip.

CLOSE ON JONATHAN

Over by the dip. He shakes his head.

                     JONATHAN
          No thanks. I'm good.

CONTINUED

53   CONTINUED: (2)   53

RESUME
                         XANDER
              Maybe you don't want to hear it,
              Buffy. But taking off like that was
              selfish and stupid-

Buffy's breaking down. It's all too much.

                         BUFFY
              Okay - I screwed up! I know it -
              alright!? But you have no idea. You
              have no idea what happened to me or
              what I was feeling-

                         XANDER
              Did you even try talking to anybody?

                         BUFFY
              What's the point? There was nothing
              anyone could do. I just had to deal
              on my own.

                         XANDER
              And you see how well that went. You
              can't just bury stuff, Buffy! It'll
              come right back up to get you...

54   INT./EXT. GILES' CAR - NIGHT   54

The zombie holding Giles rises into a close up, gruesome
proof of Xander's statement.

The other zombies are closing in as Giles finally breaks free
of the zombie's grip. He scrambles back to his car. He
PULLS THE DOOR CLOSED - overpowering the ZOMBIE who TUGS at
the handle. He slams the lock down and frantically fumbles
for his keys while the zombies ROCK his car and pound at the
windows.

Then Giles sees something. Stops.

WHAT HE SEES

Outside - his KEYS GLISTEN ON THE PAVEMENT.

BACK ON GILES

                         GILES
                      (darkly)
              Good show, Giles.

                                               CONTINUED

54 CONTINUED: 54

A beat as his mind races. Then he starts to fiddle under the
dash, YANKS some wires out. He's HOT WIRING the car.

Now a ZOMBIE SMASHES THROUGH his car window - hand
flailing - reaching for the door lock. A desperate moment
before the CAR STARTS. Giles looks pleased with himself
despite the tense circumstances. He drives off, CASTING THE
ZOMBIES ASIDE-

                    GILES (cont'd)
          Like riding a bloody bicycle.

55 INT. BUFFY'S HOUSE - LIVING ROOM - NIGHT   55

Back at the ranch - the "party" continues...

                    BUFFY
          As if I could have gone to you,
          Xander. You made your feelings about
          me and Angel pretty clear-

                    XANDER
          Look - I'm sorry your honey was a
          demon, but most girls don't hop a
          Greyhound over boy trouble!

Unexpectedly, CORDELIA steps forward.

                    CORDELIA
          Time out, Xand. I mean, put yourself
          in Buffy's shoes for a minute. I'm
          Buffy - freak of nature - right?
          Naturally, I pick a freak for a
          boyfriend... Then he's Mister
          Killing Spree, which is pretty much
          my fault, and --

                    BUFFY
               (interrupting)
          Cordy. Get out of my shoes.

                    CORDELIA
          I'm just trying to help. If you
          haven't noticed, Buffy, people aren't
          exactly lining up to give you props-

                    WILLOW
          Buffy, you never --

                    BUFFY
               (overloaded)
          Will, just - stop, okay? I can't --

                                                    CONTINUED

55 CONTINUED: 55

                              XANDER
                    Let her finish! You owe her that at
                    least!

                              BUFFY
                         (to Xander)
                    God, Xander! Do you think you could
                    stick to annoying me on your own
                    behalf?

                              XANDER
                    Fine. You stop acting like an
                    idiot - I'll stop annoying you!

                              BUFFY
                    Let's talk acting like an idiot -
                    "Nighthawk!"

Xander and Buffy actually start to get in each other's
face - like things could get physical. Oz gets between them.

                              OZ
                    Okay. Stepping in now. Being
                    referee guy-

Now Willow shouts over all of them - losing it.

                              WILLOW
                    Let them go, Oz. Talking about it
                    isn't helping; we might as well try
                    some violence!

A ZOMBIE COMES CRASHING THROUGH A LIVING ROOM WINDOW - while
the rest of the zombie army POUNDS at the doors and windows,
also trying to get inside.

Instant and TOTAL MAYHEM ENSUES. Glass flies everywhere.
The remaining party guests SCREAM and SCATTER, a few making
it out the front door.

                              WILLOW (cont'd)
                    I was being sarcastic!

CLOSE ON THE STONER DUDE

Who snaps out of his mellow daze and heads for the door.
Only to run RIGHT INTO THE ZOMBIE - who grabs the stoner dude
and SNAPS HIS NECK in one powerful, swift motion. He drops
the stoner like a rag doll and moves on.

56   INT. BUFFY'S HOUSE - KITCHEN - NIGHT   56

As ZOMBIES NOISILY SMASH through the windows and door.

57   INT. BUFFY'S HOUSE - LIVING ROOM - NIGHT   57

Everyone reacts to the sound in the kitchen. Without even
thinking - Willow, Xander, Buffy, Oz, and Cordelia respond to
the crisis by coming together. Instinct kicks in and they
are back to functioning like a fine oiled machine. Buffy
grabs a fireplace poker - tosses it to XANDER.

                    BUFFY
          Xander! The kitchen!

With cool precision, Xander snatches the poker from the air.

                    XANDER
          Got your back.

He and Cordy move off.

ON BUFFY

Who FIGHTS THE ZOMBIE with all her might - but no matter how
hard she hits it - it just keeps coming. Despite her
wiggins, Joyce GRABS A VASE and BREAKS it over the ZOMBIE'S
HEAD. Natch - it doesn't faze Mr. Zombo a bit. Joyce shouts
to Buffy-

                    JOYCE
          Are - are these vampires?

                    BUFFY
          I don't think so-

ON WILLOW

Who runs and grabs a piece of broken window frame, breaks off
a makeshift stake. She calls to Buffy-

                    WILLOW
          Buffy! Heads up!

And she throws the stake to-   *

BUFFY

Who grabs it and SLAMS IT INTO THE ZOMBIE'S HEART. Nothing
happens. She looks to Joyce-

                    BUFFY
          Nope. Not vampires.

58   INT. BUFFY'S HOUSE - FOYER - NIGHT   58

PAT, terrified, inches for the front door. She doesn't see
the ZOMBIE emerging from the hall until it's too late.   He
grabs her - silencing her with a rotting hand over her mouth.

59   INT. BUFFY'S HOUSE - KITCHEN - NIGHT   59

Xander and Cordy battle a zombie who has made it all the way
into the kitchen. Xander CONKS IT REPEATEDLY WITH THE FROZEN
SCHNAPPS BOTTLE while Cordy grabs a BARBECUE FORK and SKEWERS
IT. All to no avail.

                    XANDER
          Man, this sucker wobbles but he won't
          fall down!

60   INT. BUFFY'S HOUSE - LIVING ROOM - NIGHT   60

More zombies try to get inside the house - but Buffy and the
others keep BEATING THEM BACK.

ON DEVON AND JONATHAN   *

As Jonathan grabs one of the band's GUITARS to beat zombies   *
with.

                    DEVON
          Not my guitar! Use the bass.

ON BUFFY, WILLOW, ET AL, who still battle the zombie that
Buffy staked earlier.

                    WILLOW
          He just keeps coming!

                    BUFFY
          I know. Try to get him back outside-

Willow and Joyce wrestle the nasty looking dude toward teh
front door. OZ grabs the door handle.   *

                    JOYCE
          On three!
               (then)
          One... Two... THREE!

HE SWINGS OPEN THE DOOR AND BEATS the zombies who try to
enter back with a heavy brass candle stick. Joyce and Willow
HERD the ZOMBIE out the door. Then THEY ALL LEAN ON THE DOOR
until it closes.

ON BUFFY

                                                    CONTINUED

60   CONTINUED: 60

Who marshals Devon, Jonathan, and some terrified party guests.   *

                         BUFFY
              Help me barricade. Come on!

The guests start piling furniture, etc., against the broken   *
windows.

61   INT. BUFFY'S HOUSE - KITCHEN - NIGHT   61

Xander and Cordy have pinned Mr. Zombie on the floor and are
tying his hands and legs together with phone cord.

                        XANDER
              I got it - go help Buffy!

Cordy moves off.

62   INT. BUFFY'S HOUSE - LIVING ROOM - CONTINUOUS - NIGHT   62

Cordy enters as the others finish with the barricade. Their
fortress seems to be holding and everyone breathes a sigh of
relief.

                        BUFFY
              Great. Good job every-

SMASH! The barricade comes TUMBLING DOWN AND IT'S
ZOMBIE-RAMAA AGAIN. Everyone freaks, scatters. DEVON,
JONATHAN and other misc. guests (non-speaking extras,   *
alright?) beat it out of the living room and into the-

63   INT. BUFFY'S HOUSE - FOYER - CONTINUOUS - NIGHT   63

- where they race down the hall. Now Buffy enters and
encounters XANDER returning from the kitchen. She grabs him
as she calls to the others.

                        BUFFY
              Upstairs!

OZ and CORDY help Joyce go up the stairs before them - and
end up running right into a ZOMBIE WHO COMES CRASHING THROUGH
THE FRONT DOOR, forcing them to change directions.

                       CORDELIA
              Oh, goody. Back to the basement.

                                                      CONTINUED

64   INT. HALLWAY OUTSIDE BASEMENT DOOR - NIGHT   64

JONATHAN, DEVON, and the other guests escape into the   *
basement - closing the door just before CORDY and OZ arrive.
Oz and Cordy pound on the door, but it won't open.

                    CORDELIA
          Come on! Let us in. It's Cordelia
          and Oz-

65   INT. BUFFY'S HOUSE - BASEMENT STAIRS - CONT. - NIGHT   65

JONATHAN AND DEVON LEAN against the door - terrified.   *

                    JONATHAN
          How do we know you're not a zombie
          pretending to be Cordelia?

66   INT. HALLWAY OUTSIDE BASEMENT DOOR - CONTINUOUS - NIGHT   66

                    CORDELIA
          Zombies don't talk!

67   INT. BUFFY'S HOUSE - BASEMENT STAIRS - CONT. - NIGHT   67

Jonathan and Devon exchange glances.   *

                    DEVON
          But - how do we know? Maybe they do
          in real life. Maybe only
          pretend zombies don't talk!

68   INT. HALLWAY OUTSIDE BASEMENT DOOR - CONTINUOUS - NIGHT   68

                    CORDELIA
                    (confused)
          Well - maybe they talk in real life
          but I think they would have dapper,
          sort of a gravelly voice --

OZ notes the LARGE ZOMBIE lumbering toward them.

                    OZ
          Zombology can wait-

And her DRAGS HER AWAY.

69   INT. BUFFY'S HOUSE - STAIRWAY - NIGHT   69

Buffy, Joyce and Willow encounter PAT'S UNCONSCIOUS BODY on
the stairs as they run for safety. She moans, barely alive.
They collect her and run into-

70   INT. JOYCE'S BEDROOM - CONTINUOUS - NIGHT   70

Where they barricade themselves anew, shoving the dresser,
the bed - anything they can get their hands on - in front of
the door. Joyce and Willow move to a corner with Pat.

CLOSE ON WILLOW AND JOYCE

Willow checks Pat's Pulse. She looks at Joyce - alarmed.

                    WILLOW
          She's...

                    JOYCE
          Oh my god.

But they have no time to deal because they see that BUFFY AND
XANDER are struggling with a zombie who has WEAKENED THE
BARRICADE. Xander gets thrown back and into the opposite
wall - knocking THE CEREMONIAL MASK TO THE FLOOR.

CLOSE ON THE MASK

As the EYES START TO GLOW

RESUME

Willow and Joyce reluctantly leave Pat and go once more into
the fray.

                    JOYCE (cont'd)
                    (worried)
          What do we do if they get in?

                    XANDER
          I kind of think we die.

They are all so zombie-occupied that they don't notice-

PAT

AS HER EYES SNAP OPEN.

                                        BLACK OUT.

                    END OF ACT THREE

ACT FOUR

71   INT. BUFFY'S HOUSE - CLOSET - NIGHT   71

It's totally DARK. Two voices rise from the blackness.

                    CORDELIA (O.C.)
          Is that your foot?

                    OZ (O.C.)
          Oh. Sorry.

                    CORDELIA (O.C.)
          I don't hear anything. Should we
          check?

                    OZ (O.C.)
          Go for it.

72   INT. BUFFY'S HOUSE - HALLWAY OUTSIDE CLOSET - NIGHT   72

Oz and Cordy peer out of the closet - both holding SKI POLES
as weapons. They can HEAR activity UPSTAIRS - but there's no
zombie action. They cautiously round a corner, running right
into GILES. Everyone yells with surprise and Cordy RAISES
her pole to strike him, but Giles stops her with-

                    GILES
          Cordelia - it's me!

                    CORDELIA
          How do we know it's really you and
          not zombie Giles?

                    GILES
               (exasperated)
          Cordelia - do stop being tiresome!

                    CORDELIA
          That's him.

Cordelia lowers the pole. Oz addresses Giles.

                    OZ
          I think the dead man's Party has
          moved upstairs.

Giles nods as they move down the hall to look up the stairs.

                    GILES
          It makes sense. It's the mask in
          Joyce's bedroom they're after.

                                              CONTINUED

72   CONTINUED: 72

                              CORDELIA
                    Mask?   They're here to exfoliate?

                              GILES
                        (ignoring her)
                    The mask holds the power of a zombie
                    demon called Ovu Mobani - "evil eye."
                        (re: sitch upstairs)
                    I don't think we can get past them.

                              OZ
                    What happens if they get the mask?

                              GILES
                    If one of them puts it on... he'll be
                    the demon incarnate.

                              CORDELIA
                    Worse than a Zombie.

                              GILES
                    Worse.

Off their worried faces.

73   INT. JOYCE'S BEDROOM - NIGHT   73

Buffy, Joyce, Willow and Xander fend off A ZOMBIE who has now
broken through the barricade.

CLOSE ON THE MASK

Its eyes still GLOWING RED.

CLOSE ON ZOMBIE PAT

Who rises - slowly. Deliberately.

JOYCE

Sees her - gasps with relief and moves to her.

                              JOYCE
                    Oh, God - Pat! We thought you were-

But PAT SHOVES HER ROUGHLY ASIDE AND falls on THE MASK. She
raises it to her face and her eyes instantly FLASH RED. The   *
mask now MELDS into PAT'S FACE and becomes her DEMONIC VISAGE.   *

The other zombie in the room HITS THE FLOOR, cowering and
bowing to PAT.

                                                      CONTINUED

73   CONTINUED: 73

Xander glances nervously at Joyce - filling her in.

                    XANDER
          Generally speaking? When the scary
          things get scared? Not good.

Zombie Pat stands - surging with NEWFOUND POWER. She speaks   *
in a creepy, garbled tone.

                    ZOMBIE PAT
          I live.
               (looking at the
                others)
          You die.

NOW PAT'S EYES BEGIN TO GLOW - emitting the same eerie light   *
that came from the mask. Buffy starts toward her - but Pat   *
immediately turns her gaze on her and her eyes FLASH an even   *
BRIGHTER RED. This has a PARALYZING EFFECT, STOPPING A   *
PERPLEXED BUFFY IN HER TRACKS.

BOOM! Pat BRUTALLY BACKHANDS a defenseless Buffy - who goes
sprawling. Now Pat turns toward a cowering WILLOW. Buffy,
recovering, sees this-

                    BUFFY
          Don't look, Willow!

But it's too late. Pat looks at Willow, eyes FLASHING again,   *
and Willow is caught like a deer in Pat's headlights. Pat   *
snatches Willow from her hiding place - moves to snap her
neck.

ON BUFFY

                    BUFFY (cont'd)
          No!

Buffy lowers her head, turns her eyes away - and POWERS INTO
ZOMBIE PAT. Willow falls to the floor as Buffy plows Zombie
Pat THROUGH ONE OF THE WINDOWS.

74   EXT. BACKYARD - NIGHT   74

Buffy and Zombie Pat ROLL OFF the ROOF and land in the yard
with a horrible THUD.

75   INT. BUFFY'S HOUSE - FOYER - CONTINUOUS - NIGHT   75

Giles, Oz and Cordy are heading upstairs - but stop as they
hear Buff's dramatic fall.

                                                  CONTINUED

75   CONTINUED: 75

                         GILES
                    Out back!

They turn back but now find the bottom of the stairs BLOCKED
BY A HULKING ZOMBIE.

76   EXT. BACKYARD - NIGHT   76

Buffy and Zombie Pat recover from their plunge. Pat's eyes   *
FLASH, trying to hit Buffy again with her PARALYZING POWER,   *
but Buffy scrambles away from her - covering her eyes with
her arm.

                         BUFFY
               Not looking. Not looking...

77   INT. JOYCE'S BEDROOM - NIGHT   77

Joyce, Xander, and Willow are also occupied - struggling to
overcome the ZOMBIE still in the room with them.

Joyce manages to reach under the bed - unearth a BASEBALL BAT
she's hidden there. She now WAILS on el zombo with the bat.

78   EXT. BACKYARD - NIGHT   78

Buffy's regained her footing when Zombie Pat TACKLES HER,
sending her back to the ground. Still, even with her eyes   *
SQUEEZED SHUT, Buffy gets her feet under Zombie Pat and   *
heaves Pat off of her.

79   INT. BUFFY'S HOUSE - FOYER - NIGHT   79

Giles, Cordy and Oz are on the stairs, still detained by the
hulking zombie. OZ manages to get clear to jump over the
railing onto the hall floor. Giles shouts to him-

                         GILES
                    Oz! Tell Buffy - Moboni's power is
                    in his eyes. She has to go for the
                    eyes to defeat him!

Oz nods - escapes - just avoiding a KILLER BLOW from the
zombie.

80   EXT. BACKYARD - NIGHT   80

Zombie Pat is coming back from the blow Buffy just dealt her,
as Buffy crawls across the ground searching wildly for
something.

CLOSE ON DIGGING SPADE.

As Buffy's hand seizes it.

ON BUFFY

Who looks up - and right into the FLASHING EYES of PAT, who   *
now stands over her. Buffy is STUCK, MOTIONLESS...

ON OZ

Who arrives on the scene.

                         OZ
               Buffy!

PAT

Spins at the sound of Oz's voice.

BUFFY

Jumps to her feet.

                       BUFFY
               Hey - Pat!

Zombie Pat turns back to Buffy. Buffy LOOKS AWAY as she
DRIVES THE SPADE INTO ZOMBIE PAT'S EYES.

                    BUFFY (cont'd)
               Made you look.

A beat and then Buffy's action causes an INTENSE WHITE FLASH
that VAPORIZES ZOMBIE PAT.

81   INT. JOYCE'S BEDROOM - NIGHT   81

FLASH! Willow, Xander and Joyce react as the zombie they
were fighting DISAPPEARS.

82   INT. BUFFY'S HOUSE - FOYER - NIGHT   82

FLASH! The hulking zombie Giles and Cordy battled is
history.

83   EXT. BACKYARD - NIGHT   83

Zombie Pat is gone. It's over. No zombies. Nothing.   *

ON OZ

                         OZ
              Never mind.

A84 INT. BUFFY'S HOUSE - FOYER - CONTINUOUS - NIGHT   A84

Oz and Buffy come back into the house. Buffy is shaken and
looking a little worse for the wear.

JOYCE, WILLOW, GILES, XANDER and CORDY move to them,
concerned.

                       JOYCE
              Honey - Are you alright?

Buffy reaches for her mother.

                       BUFFY
              Mom-

And they hug. Holding on tight. Finally, the break apart-

                       JOYCE
              So is this... a typical day at the
              office?

                       BUFFY
              This? No.
                    (only half-kidding)
              This was nothing.

Joyce looks appalled, but doesn't really have a chance to
react before XANDER moves to Buffy - his tone concilatory.

                       XANDER
              Nice moves.

                       BUFFY
              You too.

They slap hands, low and casual, sealing an unspoken truce.
Now WILLOW, CORDY, and OZ also crowd around for more hugs and
words of encouragement.

                                              CONTINUED

A84 CONTINUED: A84

CLOSE ON GILES

Who stands slightly apart from the others. Watching the
group come together and enfold Buffy. He's clearly moved,
but somethng else crosses his features - resolve.

84 INT. PRINCIPAL SNYDER'S OFFICE - DAY   84

GILES knocks - looks in. Snyder looks up from his desk -
annoyed.

                    PRINCIPAL SNYDER
              Did we have an appointment?

Giles closes the door. Steps inside.

                    GILES
              I'd like to have a word with you.

Snyder moves from behind his desk - grabs a folder.

                    PRINCIPAL SNYDER
              If that word is "Buffy" - then I have
              two words for you. Good riddance.
                    (then)
              Now. If you don't mind. I have an
              appointment with the mayor...

                    GILES
              You can't keep her out of this school.

                    PRINCIPAL SNYDER
              I think you'll find I can.

                    GILES
              You have no grounds for expelling her.

                    PRINCIPAL SNYDER
              I have grounds, I have precedent, and
              this tingly kind of --

                    GILES
              It won't hold. Buffy Summers is a
              minor and entitled to a public
              education. Your personal distaste
              for the girl does not legally enable
              you --

                    PRINCIPAL SNYDER
              Why don't you take it up with the
              city council?

                                                      CONTINUED

84   CONTINUED: 84

He starts out of the office, stopping right between Giles and
the wall as Giles says:

                    GILES
          I thought I'd start with the State
          supreme court. You may be powerful
          in local circles, but I believe I can
          make life very uncomfortable for you.
          Professionally speaking. And Buffy
          Summers will be allowed back in.

A moment, then Snyder regains an appearance of superiority.

                    PRINCIPAL SNYDER
          Sorry. I'm not convinced.

Giles puts his hand to Snyder's chest and SLAMS HIM UP
AGAINST THE WALL with one violent, swift motion. He looks
coldly down at the man, all Ripper.

                    GILES
          Do you want me to convince you?

OFF SNYDER - stunned, about to backtrack massively...

                                        FADE TO:

85   EXT. COFFEE HOUSE - SHOPPING DISTRICT - DAY   85

The place Willow stood Buffy up earlier.

86   INT. COFFEE HOUSE - DAY   86

A cozy, bustling place.

ON BUFFY AND WILLOW

Who sit at a table, scraping up the last of a shared (big
chocolatey messy) dessert). Totally oblivious to the world
around them. We catch them mid-conversation.

                    WILLOW
          I mean I'm not a full fledged
          witch, that takes years. I just did
          a couple of pagan blessings and teeny
          glamour to hide a zit.

                    BUFFY
          It doesn't scare you?

                                        CONTINUED

86 CONTINUED: 86

                              WILLOW
              It has. I tried to communicate with
              the spirit world and I so wasn't
              ready for that. It was like being
              pulled apart inside. Plus I blew the
              power for our whole block. Big scare.

                              BUFFY
              Oh, I wish I coulda been there with
              you.

                              WILLOW
              Me too. I really freaked out.

                              BUFFY
              I'm sorry...

                              WILLOW
              It's okay. Really, I understand you
              having to bail and I can forgive
              that. I have to make allowances for
              what you're going through and just be
              a grown up about it.

Beat.

                              BUFFY
              You're loving this moral superiority
              thing.

                              WILLOW
              It's like a drug.

                              BUFFY
              Fine. I'm the bad, I can take my
              lumps. For a while.

                              WILLOW
              All right, I'll stop giving you a
              hard time.
                      (beat)
              Runaway.

                              BUFFY
              Will...

                              WILLOW
              I'm sorry.
                      (beat)
              Quitter.

                                                        CONTINUED

CONTINUED: (2)   86

> BUFFY
> (beat)

Whiner.

> WILLOW

Bailer.

> BUFFY

Harpy.

> WILLOW

Delinquent.

> BUFFY

Tramp.

                                                    BLACK OUT.

> WILLOW (V.O.)

Bad seed.

> BUFFY (V.O.)

Witch.

                    THE END

BUFFY THE VAMPIRE SLAYER

"Faith, Hope & Trick"

Written By

David Greenwalt

Directed By

James A. Contner

SHOOTING SCRIPT

August 5, 1998   (WHITE)
August 7, 1998   (BLUE)
August 10, 1998   (PINK)
August 11, 1998   (YELLOW)
August 13, 1998   (GREEN)
August 17, 1998   (GOLDENROD)
September 9, 1998   (SALMON)

BUFFY THE VAMPIRE SLAYER

"Faith, Hope & Trick"

CAST LIST

```
BUFFY SUMMERS......................... Sarah Michelle Gellar
XANDER HARRIS........................ Nicholas Brendon
RUPERT GILES........................ Anthony S. Head
WILLOW ROSENBERG..................... Alyson Hannigan
CORDELIA CHASE....................... Charisma Carpenter
ANGEL............................... David Boreanaz
OZ.................................. Seth Green

JOYCE............................... Kristine Sutherland
PRINCIPAL SNYDER.................... Armin Shimerman
FAITH.............................. Eliza Dushku
MR. TRICK.......................... K. Todd Freeman
KAKISTOS........................... Jeremy Roberts
SCOTT HOPE......................... Fab Filippo
MANAGER...........................*John Ennis
PIZZA GUY.........................*Robert David Price
VAMP 3.............................
TAKE-OUT GUY.......................
```

BUFFY THE VAMPIRE SLAYER

"Faith, Hope & Trick"

SET LIST

INTERIORS

BUFFY'S HOUSE
    BUFFY'S BEDROOM
    DINING ROOM
    KITCHEN
SUNNYDALE HIGH SCHOOL
    PRINCIPAL SNYDER'S OFFICE
    HALLWAY
    LIBRARY
    LOUNGE
    HALL NEAR LOUNGE
THE BRONZE
ABANDONED FIREHOUSE
LIMOUSINE
CHEESY MOTEL ROOM
MANSION

EXTERIORS

SUNNYDALE HIGH SCHOOL
HAPPY BURGER
THE BRONZE
ABANDONED FIREHOUSE
SUNNYDALE STREETS
CHEESY MOTEL
STREET
ANOTHER STREET
MANSION
*CONSTRUCTION SITE

BUFFY THE VAMPIRE SLAYER

"Faith, Hope & Trick"

TEASER

1   EXT. SUNNYDALE HIGH - DAY   1

Lunch time. Students mill.

TWO FEET - Teeter on the curb.

WILLOW - looks down at her feet, Oz next to her. Cordelia and
Xander (holding hands) approach in b.g.

>   WILLOW
>   I'm giddy.

>   OZ
>   Like you giddy. Always have.

>   WILLOW
>   It's the freedom! As Seniors we can
>   go off campus now for lunch. It's no
>   longer cutting, it's legal. Heck,
>   it's expected. But also a big step
>   forward, a Senior Moment...

Oz glances over his shoulder at Xander, they exchange nods.

>   WILLOW (cont'd)
>   ...one that has to be savored fully
>   before -- ooo!

Withought breaking stride, Xander takes Willow's arm as Oz
takes the other. They carry her off the curb, towards the
park across the street.

>   WILLOW (cont'd)
>   I can't.

>   XANDER
>   You can.

>   OZ
>   See? You are.

CONTINUED

1   CONTINUED: 1

                         WILLOW
               But... what if they changed the rule
               without telling? What if they're
               laying in wait just so they can
               arrest me and put me in detention and
               mar my unblemished record?

                         XANDER
               Breathe.

                         WILLOW
               Okay. You can put me down.
                         (they do; she links
                          her arm through Oz's)
               Better now. Wow. We're seniors. Hey,
               we're walkin' here!
                         (then:)
               Maybe we shouldn't be too couply
               around Buffy.

                         CORDELIA
               Oh, you mean 'cause of how the only
               guy that ever liked her turned into
               a vicious killer and had to be put
               down like a dog?

                         XANDER
               Can she cram complex issues into a
               nutshell or what?

                         OZ
               Prepare to uncouple... uncouple.

     The four of them unlink hands and arms as they enter the --

2   EXT. PARK - DAY   2

ANGLE - BUFFY BY A BENCH IN THE PARK

Willow, Xander, Cordelia and Oz (uncoupled) approach. Other
STUDENTS eat and mingle in b.g.

                         XANDER
               Buffy, banned from campus but not
               from our hearts, how are you and
               what's for lunch?

                         BUFFY
               I just threw together a few things...

                                                        CONTINUED

2   CONTINUED: 2

She pulls paper towels off a couple of platters revealing a
stunning array of cold cuts, sliced fruit, breads, etc. They
munch as:

                    CORDELIA
          When did you become Martha Stewart?

                    BUFFY
          First of all, Martha Stewart knows
          jack about hand-cut prosciutto.

                    XANDER
          I don't believe she slays, either.

                    OZ
          I hear she can, but she doesn't like
          to.

                    BUFFY
          Second of all... way too much time on
          my hands since I got kicked out of
          school.

                    WILLOW
          I know they'll let you back in.

                    XANDER
          Don't you and your mom have a meeting
          with Principal Snyder?

                    BUFFY
               (nods)
          We're seeing Snyde-man tomorrow.
          Maybe I should bring a wheel of my
          extra runny brie...

Willow sees: SCOTT HOPE, nice guy Senior, heading their way.

                    WILLOW
               (to Buffy)
          Scott Hope at eleven o'clock.
               (as Buffy looks)
          He likes you, he wanted to ask you
          out last year, you weren't ready then
          but I think you're ready now -- or at
          least in a state of pre-readiness
          that would allow you to make
          conversation or do that thing with
          your mouth that boys like --
               (more)

                                                          CONTINUED

2 CONTINUED: (2)   2

                    WILLOW (cont'd)
                  (sudden panic)
          I don't mean a bad thing with your
          mouth, I mean that sort of half smile
          that you do and --
                  (beat; to Oz:)
          You're s'posed to stop me when I do
          that.

                    OZ
          I like it when you do that.

                    SCOTT
                  (passing by)
          Hi Buffy.

                    BUFFY
          Hi.

And he's gone.

                    WILLOW
          Oh, I think that went very well.
                  (to the others)
          Don't you think that went very well?

                    CORDELIA
          He didn't try to slit our throats or
          anything, it's progress.

                    WILLOW
                  (to Buffy)
          Did you do the half smile?

                    BUFFY
          I'm not trying to snare Scott Hope,
          Will. I just want to get my life
          back, okay? Do normal stuff.

                    WILLOW
          Like date...

                    BUFFY
          Well...

                    XANDER
          Oh, you wanna date. I saw that half-
          smile, you slut.

                                                        CONTINUED

2   CONTINUED: (3)   2

Laughing, Buffy punches Xander in the arm. He laughs as well
til he realizes how much that --

                         XANDER (cont'd)
              Ow.

-- hurt.

                         BUFFY
              All right, yes. Date. Shop. Go to
              school, hang out, save the world from
              unspeakable demons -- I wanna do all
              that girl stuff.

3   EXT. HAPPY BURGER - NIGHT   3

CRANE DOWN on the drive-thru joint, past Mr. "Happy Burger"
himself (half man, half burger, big grinning plastic face) as
a long, black limo glides to the order window. We hear:

                         TAKE-OUT GUY (V.O.)
              Welcome to Happy Burger, can I take
              your order?

And the silky voice of:

                         MR. TRICK
              Diet soda. Medium. Thank you.

                         TAKE-OUT GUY (V.O.)
              That will be eighty-nine cents at the
              window, sir.

THE LIMO - We catch a glimpse of MR. TRICK as the darkened
window rolls back up. He is young (20's), smart, easygoing
and deadly. Speaks quickly and mellifluously, all charm.

4
     INT. LIMOUSINE - NIGHT   4

Mr. Trick sits in back next to a shape silhouetted in the
darkness. In some circles he is worshipped, in all he is   *
feared. He is KAKISTOS.

                         MR. TRICK
              Sunnydale. Town's got quaint, and the
              people: he called me sir, don't you
              miss that?
                         (more)

                                                          CONTINUED

4   CONTINUED: 4

                         MR. TRICK (cont'd)
                    Admittedly, no a haven for the
                    brothers -- strictly the caucasian
                    persuasion in the Dale -- but you
                    gotta stand up and salute their death
                    rate. I ran a statistical analysis
                    and Hello Darkness -- makes D.C. look
                    like Mayberry. And nobody sayin' boo
                    about it. We could fit right in
                    here. Have some fun.

Kakistos lays a hand on Trick's arm. The hand is cloven,   *
beastly.

                         KAKISTOS
                    We're here for one thing.

                         MR. TRICK
                    Kill the Slayer, I know. Still, big
                    picture.

Trick rolls down the window, pays the guy inside.

                         TAKE-OUT GUY
                    Have a nice night.

                         MR. TRICK
                    Right back at you.

                         KAKISTOS
                    I'm going to rip her spine out of her
                    body, then I'm going to eat her heart
                    and suck the marrow from her bones.

                         MR. TRICK
                         (beat)
                    And now I'm hungry.

5   EXT. HAPPY BURGER - NIGHT   5

Trick reaches out his window. The TAKE-OUT GUY'S smile turns
to terror when he sees TRICK HAS BECOME a <u>vamp</u>.

TRICK'S HAND

Vises's the guy's throat, rips him <u>out the drive-thru window</u>.
The guy screams bloody murder as:

THE LIMO

                                                          CONTINUED

5 CONTINUED: 5

    Peels out, the guy's legs hanging out the back window, his
    screams growing distant as we settle on Mr. Happy Burger,
    grinning his eternal plastic grin.

                                              BLACK OUT.

                        END OF TEASER

ACT ONE

6 EXT. BRONZE - NIGHT - ESTABLISHING   6

7 INT. BRONZE - NIGHT   7

Small crowd. Cordelia, Oz, Willow, Xander at a table.
Watching (with no particular emotion) something on the dance
floor. We PUSH PAST THEM and discover:

BUFFY AND ANGEL - Slow dancing, holding onto one another
tenderly.

                    BUFFY
          I miss you.

Buffy looks up at Angel, he looks at her, then turns his
head, she follows his gaze to:

HER HAND, ON HIS SHOULDER

And the ring her gave her.

THE RING

Slips off Buffy's finger and CLATTERS TO THE FLOOR (Possible
slo-mo.)

Angel picks up the ring. Looks at Buffy. PUSH TO BUFFY --

-- FLASHCUTS: Episode 22, YEAR 2 - She runs the sword through
him; he is sucked into hell --

IN THE BRONZE - Her friends stare expressionlessly.

                    BUFFY (cont'd)
          I had to...

He tightens his fingers around the ring, crushing it; Buffy
sees a bit of blood trickle from his fist to the floor.

                    ANGEL
          I loved you...

She looks at his chest where she ran the sword through, his
shirt red now with seeping blood. She moves towards him:

                    BUFFY
          Oh god, Angel...

                                              CONTINUED

7   CONTINUED: 7

                              ANGEL
                    GO TO HELL!

His fury stops her in her tracks. Then he smiles. And it's
not a pleasant smile.

And his face is now a horrible ROTTING CORPSE MASK.

                              ANGEL (CONT'D)
                    I did.

Buffy screams and screams.

8   INT. BUFFY'S BEDROOM - MORNING (DAY)   8

Buffy bolts up in bed from her nightmare. Breathing hard. She
takes a moment to get her bearings. Something catches her
eye: on the bed post, hung with the scarves and other things,
a long silver chain -- on it the RING Angel gave her. She
reaches out to touch the ring. Stops, startled by:

                              JOYCE (V.O.)
                    Morning, sunshine...

Joyce is in the doorway.

                              JOYCE
                    Ready to face the beast?

9   INT. SCHOOL - SNYDER'S OFFICE - DAY   9

SNYDER, the aforementioned beast, faces Buffy and Joyce.

                         PRINCIPAL SNYDER
                    Here are the terms of your re-entry,
                    Missy, take 'em or leave 'em.

Buffy flips (or picks up) a dagger-like silver letter opener
off the edge of Snyder's desk, toying with it as:

                                                         CONTINUED

9 CONTINUED: 9

                    PRINCIPAL SNYDER (cont'd)
          One: you pass a make-up test for each
          class you skipped out on last year;
          two: you provide, in writing, one
          glowing recommendation from any
          member of our faculty who is not an
          English librarian; three: you
          complete an interview with the school
          psychologist who must conclude that
          your violent tendencies...

Snyder quickly but cautiously removes the letter opener from
Buffy's grasp.

                    PRINCIPAL SNYDER (cont'd)
          ...are under control.

                    JOYCE
          I'm not sure I like your attitude,
          Mr. Snyder. I spoke to the School
          Board and according to them --

                    PRINCIPAL SNYDER
          -- I'm required to educate every
          juvenile who's not in jail where she
          belongs.
                    (to Buffy)
          Welcome back.

He opens the door for them to leave. As they do:

                    BUFFY
          So, I'm really back because the
          School Board overruled you...
                    (nothing from Snyder)
          ...wow, that's like having our whole
          ability to do this job called into
          question when you think about it.

Snyder stares sullenly at the girl.

                    JOYCE
          I think what my daughter's trying to
          say is: nyah nyah nyah nyah.   *

They leave.

                                                       CONTINUED

9   CONTINUED: (2)   9

                         SECRETARY (O.S.)
                 It's the mayor on line one.   ★
                                                               ★

      As dread shows on Snyder's face...   ★

10   OMITTED   10

11   INT. LIBRARY - DAY   11

Empty. Willow and Buffy enter.

                    WILLOW
          It's so great you're a school girl   *
          again.   *
                                                        *

                    BUFFY
          What did Giles want, was he mad?   *
                                                        *

                    WILLOW
               (looks around)
          I don't think so, he just needed to
          see you. Have you ever noticed when   *
          he is mad but he's too English to say   *
          anything he makes that weird "cluck
          cluck" sound with his tongue --

Giles rises from the counter, a pestle and mortar in hand.

                    BUFFY
               (for Willow's benefit)
          Hi Giles.

                    WILLOW
          Oh, hi. Been there long?

Giles sets the pestle and mortar down next to some herbs on
the counter, busying himself with them as:

                    GILES
          Buffy, good timing, I can use your
          help. I trust you remember the demon
          Acathla --

                    BUFFY
          Giles, please, contain yourself. Yes,
          I'm finally back in school but you
          know how it embarrasses me when you
          gush so. Why don't we skip all
          that and get right to work.

                    GILES
          Oh, ahhh. Sorry. Of course it's
          wonderful that you're back. That goes
          without saying. But you... enjoy
          making me say it, don't you?

                                                       CONTINUED

11 CONTINUED: 11

                              BUFFY
                    That and chocolate, what else have I
                    got? So, Acathla, what ya' doin':
                              (re: mortar, herbs)
                    ...making him some demon pizza?

                              GILES
                    We need to make sure he remains
                    dormant, and the dimensional vortex
                    stays well shut. So I'm working on
                    a binding spell.

                              WILLOW
                    Ooo, a spell, can I help?

                              GILES
                    Possibly with the research. It's a
                    very sensitive --

                              WILLOW
                    Who's more sensitive than me?

                              GILES
                    -- and difficult spell.
                              (to Buffy)
                    It involves creating a protective
                    circle around... I don't want to bore
                    you, but there's a litany that one
                    recites in Aramaic. It's very
                    specific, and I need to know a few
                    things about your experience in
                    defeating Acathla and Angel.

Buffy looks a tad stony, but:

                              BUFFY
                    Fire away.

                              GILES
                    I've put the time at around 6:17,
                    about half an hour after Xander
                    rescued me...

                              BUFFY
                    Less. More like ten minutes.

                              GILES
                    And was the vortex already open?

                                                              CONTINUED

                                   128

11 CONTINUED: (2)   11

                         BUFFY
                    Just barely.

                         GILES
                    I see. And Angel...?

                         BUFFY
                    Big fight, Angel got the pointy end
                    of the sword, Acathla sucked him into
                    hell instead of the world. That's
                    about the it.

A school bell rings.

                         GILES
                    Yes. Well that should be helpful.

                         BUFFY
                    I gotta go. I've got the English
                    make-up test. You get some credit
                    just for speaking it, right?

She goes. Willow picks up a couple of the herbs.

                         WILLOW
                    Sage, love that smell... and Marnox
                    root. Just a smidge of this mixed
                    with a virgin's saliva --
                              (off his look, drops
                               root)
                    -- does something I know nothing
                    about.

                         GILES
                    These forces aren't something one
                    plays around with, Willow. What have
                    you been conjuring?

                         WILLOW
                    Nothing much. I mean, I tried that
                    spell to cure Angel, I guess that was
                    a bust, but after that just, you
                    know, small stuff. Floating feather,
                    fire out of ice, which next time I
                    won't do on the bedspread -- are you
                    mad at me?

                                                    CONTINUED

11 CONTINUED: (3)   11

                         GILES
          Of course not. If I were angry I
          believe I would be making a strange
          clucking sound with my tongue.

12 INT. BRONZE - NIGHT   12

     Start on the band (if we have one) playing something sexy.
     Drift through the dancers, lingering on a WILD GIRL (FAITH,
     young, loose and fast, 18-ish, biker type meets trailer park)
     dancing suggestively with an older GUY, mid-20's, his dance
     steps reminiscent of the seventies. Xander and Cordelia dance
     nearby.

     DOLLY to Willow and Oz at a table. They are smooching -- they   *
     brake it up as Buffy approaches with drinks.   *

                         BUFFY   *
          Don't let me interrupt...   *

     Buffy's in a good mood.   *

                         WILLOW
          Are you... is she all a glow-y?

                         OZ
          I suspect happiness.

                         BUFFY
          I passed my English make-up -- I'm
          out with my friends, hello my life,
          how I've missed you.

                         WILLOW
                    (sees Scott
                     approaching)
          Hi, Scott, what are you doing here?

     Scott, looking good, walks up.

                         SCOTT
          You told me if I came after eight I
          could run into Buffy.
                    (to Buffy)
          I'm a bad liar, it's not good for the
          soul -- or the skin: it makes me
          blotch.

                                              CONTINUED

12 CONTINUED: 12

                         BUFFY
              Hi, Scott.

                         SCOTT
              Hi. Don't you love this song?

                                                        CONTINUED

12 CONTINUED: 12

                              BUFFY
                    Actually... I do.

                              SCOTT
                         (beat)
                    Would you like to...?
                         (re: dance floor)

                              BUFFY
                    Dance? I, uh... I don't know, I
                    mean... I don't know. Thanks for
                    asking but...

                              SCOTT
                    I'm just going to go stand by the
                    dance floor. If you change your mind
                    you can mosey on over. If not, you
                    don't mosey. No harm, no foul.

He smiles and goes. Buffy watches him go.

                              WILLOW
                    Come on, Buffy, the guy is charm, and
                    normal which is that thing you want
                    to get back to.

                              OZ
                    Plus, bonus points for use of the
                    word "mosey."

                              BUFFY
                    I'm just... I'm not ready.

                              WILLOW
                    What's stopping you...?

Buffy doesn't answer.

Cordelia and Xander return from the dance floor.

                              CORDELIA
                    Check out the Slut-o-rama and her
                    Disco Dave...

Buffy looks:

BUFFY'S POV

Faith dancing with the older guy.

                                                              CONTINUED

12 CONTINUED: (2)   12

                         CORDELIA (cont'd)
                 ...what was the last thing that guy
                 danced to, K.C. and the Sunshine Band?

Buffy studies the guy as the Wild Girl drapes an arm around
his shoulder. They head for the exit.

                         BUFFY
                 I don't think that guy thrives on
                 sunshine...

Buffy moves off after them.

ANGLE - THE DANCE FLOOR

Scott sees Buffy approaching. His face lights up.

                         SCOTT
                 Hi.

                         BUFFY
                 Oh. I didn't come to... I have to...
                     (nods toward exit)

                         SCOTT
                 Sorry. My bad.

                         BUFFY
                 No. It's mine, it's mine. I really
                 gotta...

And Buffy hurries towards the exit.

13 EXT. BRONZE - NIGHT   13

Buffy exits. Looks around for the Wild Girl. Cor, Xander,
Willow and Oz exit behind her.

                         BUFFY
                 Where is she...?

                         CORDELIA
                 I bet it's nothing, they're probably
                 just making out --

SOUNDS of a violent confrontation from around the corner.

                                                        CONTINUED

13   CONTINUED: 13

                          WILLOW
               -- that's not what making out sounds
               like -- unless I'm doing it wrong...

Buffy is already charging ahead, the others follow:

14   EXT. BRONZE - DESERTED ALLEY - NIGHT   14

Buffy arrives in time to see: Faith up against a wall, her
head down in shadow and the guy -- he's a vamp all right
(VAMP 1) -- moving towards her.

The gang arrives as Buffy whips out a stake, charges in,
ready to slay. Faith brings her head up, into the light: it's
not a face full of fear, it's a face full of glee -- ready to
kick ass.

As Buffy is about to stake Vamp 1, Faith leaps in the air,
spin kicks over Buffy's head and connects with the vamp's
face, sending him reeling back and down. Faith turns to
Buffy.

                          FAITH
               S'okay, I got it. You're Buffy, right?

The vamp rises behind her.

                          FAITH (cont'd)
               I'm Faith.

Without turning around, Faith back-head butts the vamp,
smashing him back.

                          OZ
               I'm gonna go out on a limb here and
               say we've got a new slayer in town.

Faith delivers several impressive kicks and punches to Vamp
1 as the others watch, then turns back to Buffy.

                          FAITH
                        (re: stake)
               Can I borrow that?

Faith takes the stake from Buffy's hand. Then with shocking
speed and a little savageness, WHAM! she stakes Vamp 1 to
dust. She flips the stake back to Buffy.

                                                    CONTINUED

14 CONTINUED: 14

                         FAITH (cont'd)
                Thanks, B. Couldn't a done it without
                ya'.

        Faith grins, walks by Buffy. Off Buffy's look,

                                        BLACK OUT.

                        END OF ACT ONE

ACT TWO

15   INT. BRONZE - NIGHT - LATER   15

At a table; Faith devours a huge muffin, in the middle of a
story; Xander, Cor, Oz and Willow are charmed and amused by
Faith (okay, Cordelia's not charmed by anyone) -- Buffy feels
a little left out.

                    FAITH
          -- it was about a hundred and
          eighteen degrees, I'm sleepin'
          without a stich on, suddenly I hear
          all this screamin'. I go tearin'
          outside -- stark nude -- this church
          bus has broke down and three vamps
          are feasting on half the Baptists in
          South Boston. So I waste the vamps
          and the preacher is hugging me like
          there's no tomorrow when the cops
          pull up. They arrested us both.

                    XANDER
          They should film that story and show
          it every Christmas.

Faith grabs another muffin.

                    FAITH
          God, I could eat a horse!
               (to Buffy)
          Isn't it crazy? Slayin' always makes
          you just hungry and horny.

The others look at Buffy, frankly curious.

                    BUFFY
          Well... sometimes I crave a non-fat
          yogurt afterwards...

Out of the blue:

                    CORDELIA
          I get it.
               (Off their looks)
          Not the horny thing -- yuck -- the
          two slayer thing: there was only one,
          but then Buffy died for like two
          minutes so Kendra was called, then
          Kendra died so Faith was called.

                                                    CONTINUED

> WILLOW
> But why were you called here?

> FAITH
> I wasn't. My watcher went to some
> retreat thing in England, so I
> skipped out. I thought, this is my
> big chance to meet the infamous Buff
> and compare notes -- So B, did you
> really use a rocket launcher one time?

> BUFFY
> Well, it's actually funny --

> XANDER
>   (to Faith,
>   interrupting)
> What was that about the alligator?
> You said something before --

> FAITH
> Oh, this big daddy vampire out of
> Missouri kept 'em as pets. He's got
> me rasslin' one of 'em, must of been
> twelve feet long --

> XANDER
> Now, was this also naked?

> FAITH
>   (smiles)
> Well, the alligator was...

> CORDELIA
> Xander, find a new theme?

> WILLOW
>   (worried)
> Did the alligator get hurt?

> FAITH
> Only a little. Then it was dead.

> WILLOW
> Oh. No...

> FAITH
> I never had more trouble than that
> damn vamp.
>   (more)

CONTINUED

15   CONTINUED: (2)   15

                         FAITH (cont'd)
                          (to Buffy)
               What about you? What was your
               toughest kill?

ANGLE - BUFFY

FLASHCUT: Buffy runs the sword through Angel (5V22).

BACK TO SCENE

                         BUFFY
               They're all tough in different ways
               I guess...
                          (trying)
               Oh, but, do you guys remember the
               Three? Or, you never met the
               Three... But anyway --

                         OZ
               Something occurring: you both kill
               the vamps and who could argue with
               that, but --
                          (to Faith)
               I'm wondering about your position on
               werewolves.

                         WILLOW
                          (proudly)
               Oz is a werewolf.

                         BUFFY
                          (to Faith)
               Long story.

                         OZ
               Got bit.

                         BUFFY
               Apparently not that long.

                         FAITH
               Hey, as long as you don't go scratchin'
               at me or humpin' my leg, we're five
               by five.

                         OZ
               Fair enough.

                                                    CONTINUED

15 CONTINUED: (3)   15

                    FAITH
          Now the vamps, they better get their
          asses to defcon one, the two of us
          around. We're gonna have some fun
          you and me, watcher-less and fancy
          free.

                    BUFFY
          Watcher-less?

                    FAITH
          Didn't yours go to England, too?

16 EXT. SUNNYDALE HIGH - DAY - ESTABLISHING   16

                    GILES (O.S.)
          There is a watcher retreat every year
          in the Cotswalds...

17 INT. LIBRARY - DAY   17

     Giles, Buffy, Xander, Willow, Faith.

                    GILES
          ...lovely spot, very serene. They
          have horseback riding, river rafting,
          lectures and discussions. Quite an
          honor to be invited; they're very
          stimulating events.
                    (trying not to be
                     peevish)
          So I'm told...

                    FAITH
          Ah, it's boring. Way too stuffy for
          a guy like you.

                    BUFFY
          Um, maybe I should introduce you
          again. Faith, this is Giles.

                    FAITH
          I seen him. If I'd a known they came
          this young and cute I'd've requested
          a transfer.

                    BUFFY
          Okay, raise your hand if "ew."

                                                       CONTINUED

17 CONTINUED: 17

                          GILES
                    (trying not to be
                     flustered)
          Well, leaving for the moment the
          question of my youth and beauty, I
          would say it's fortuitous that Faith
          arrived when she did.

                          WILLOW
          Ah-hah!
                    (off their looks)
          Sorry, I just meant --
                    (exactly the same)
          -- ah-hah! There's a big evil
          brewing -- you'll never be bored
          here, Faith, 'cause this is
          Sunnydale, home of the big brewing
          evil.

                          GILES
          I don't know how big an evil it is at
          this point but two people have
          disappeared in the Sunset Ridge
          district.

                          XANDER
          Ah hah!
                    (to Willow)
          Fun.

                          GILES
                    (shoots Xander a
                     look, then:)
          One of them, a fast food worker, was
          pulled right out of his order window.

                          BUFFY
          I'm good to patrol. Late-ish,
          though; I promised mom I'd be home
          for dinner.

     Expectant looks from the others prompt:

                          BUFFY (cont'd)
                    (to Faith)
          To which you're invited, of course.
          Dinner. With us.

                          FAITH
          Dying to meet the fam. I'm in.

                                                        CONTINUED

17   CONTINUED: (2)   17

                    BUFFY
                (darn)
          Great. Then we'll patrol. Also
          together. Try to get a bead on these
          new vamps.

                    FAITH
                (pumped)
          We'll hunt 'em down and kill 'em
          where they stand. Come to momma, unh!

Faith mimes punching a head.

                    XANDER
          She doesn't make it sound like work
          at all.

                    WILLOW
                (to Buffy)
          Don't you have a health science make-
          up?

                    BUFFY
          Yeah, I could use a little coaching --

                    WILLOW
                (to Faith, ignoring
                 Buffy)
          You can hang with us while she's
          testing. You wanta?

                    XANDER
                (to Faith)
          Say yes and bring your stories.

                    BUFFY
          Yeah, you guys run along, I'll be
          fine, really, I'll just sit here...

                    FAITH
          Okay, have fun.
                (to Giles)
          Later on. We'll talk weapons.

The three take off, leaving Buffy with Giles.

                    GILES
          This new girl has rather a lot of
          zest.   *
                (off Buffy's look)

                                                   CONTINUED

17   CONTINUED: (3)   17

                         GILES (cont'd)
          Oh, I had a little problem with the
          binding spell for Acathla -- in fact
          I wound up with a face full of Marnox
          root. I seem to be lacking the
          requisite details to perform it
          correctly. The physical location --
          Acathla was facing south...

                         BUFFY
          Yeah.
                  (pointing and
                   demonstrating)
          Acathla. Angel. Me.
                  (mimes stabbing)
          Sword.

                         GILES
          That's what I thought, but I wonder --

                         BUFFY
          Giles, I've got make-up tests to
          pass, missing folks in Sunset Ridge,
          a zesty new slayer to feed... next
          time I kill Angel I'll video it, okay?

     Buffy goes. Giles watches her.

18   INT. SCHOOL/HALL LOUNGE - DAY - LATER   18

     Willow, Xander and Faith head down the hall past the
     cafeteria towards the lounge. They're having a good time.

                         WILLOW
          And here we have the cafeteria, where
          we were mauled by snakes...

                         XANDER
          This is the spot where Angel tried to
          kill Willow.

                         WILLOW
          Over there in the lounge is where
          Spike and his gang nearly massacred
          us all on parent-teacher night. Oh,
          and up those stairs, I was sucked
          into a muddy grave...

                                                      CONTINUED

18 CONTINUED: 18

                              XANDER
                They say young people don't learn
                anything in high school nowadays but,
                I've learned to be afraid.

                              FAITH
                You guys are a hoot 'n a half. If I'd
                had friends like you in high school,
                I'd've still dropped out but I mighta
                been sad about it.
                         (beat)
                What's up with B? She seems wound
                kinda tight -- needs to find the fun
                a little, like you two. Water.
                         (heads for fountain)

                              XANDER
                Then the alligator story!

XANDER AND WILLOW

Watch Faith as Cordelia moves up behind Xander.

                              XANDER (cont'd)
                She's got something, doesn't she?

                              CORDELIA
                         (startling him)
                What is it with you and slayers?
                Maybe I should dress you up like one and
                hold a stake to your throat.

Xander regards her hungrily for a moment:

                              XANDER
                Please, God, don't let that be
                sarcasm.

ANGLE - FAITH

As she straightens up from the water fountain, almost bumps
into:

                              SCOTT
                Excuse me.

                              FAITH
                Sorry. Hey, I seen you before.

                                                    CONTINUED

18 CONTINUED: (2)   18

                        SCOTT
              At the Bronze? You're friends with
              Buffy, right?

                        FAITH
              Yeah. I'm Faith.

                        SCOTT
              Scott, nice to meet you.

WILLOW, CORDELIA AND XANDER

As Buffy moves up.

                        BUFFY
              I'm two for two with the make-up
              tests. Proud, yes, but also humble
              in this time of --
                        (re: they're looking
                         elsewhere)
              What are we looking at?

                        CORDELIA
                        (re: Faith)
              Does anyone believe that's her actual
              hair color?

Buffy follows Cordelia's gaze to:

BUFFY'S POV - SCOTT AND FAITH

At the water fountain, out of earshot, Scott is laughing.

BACK TO SCENE

                        WILLOW
              Boy I haven't seen him laugh like
              that... maybe Faith and Scott could
              hit it off. I mean, if you're done
              with him -- not that you used him or
              anything.

                        BUFFY
              I hadn't definitely, one hundred per
              cent said no to him for all time...
              it's just, you don't enter into these
              things lightly, there's repercussions
              to consider and...

Willow and Xander exchange a knowing look.

                                                    CONTINUED

144

18   CONTINUED: (3)   18

                              BUFFY (cont'd)
                    Why am I seeing a look?

                              WILLOW
                    You really do need to find the fun a
                    little, "B"...
                              (off Buffy's look)
                    ...uffy.

          Buffy moves to --

                              SCOTT
                              (spots:)
                    Buffy, Faith is telling me tall tales.

                              BUFFY
                    She's funny. And leaving.
                              (to Faith)
                    We have to go.

                              SCOTT
                              (thinking it's him)
                    Oh.
                              (to Faith)
                    Nice talking to you.

                              FAITH
                    Likewise.
                              (as they move off)
                    Cute guy. He seeing anybody?

19   OMITTED   19   *

20   INT. ABANDONED FIREHOUSE - DAY   20

          Day (we can tell as a vamp tapes up a light-crack in one of
          the blacked out windows) but dark and gloomy. Vamps light
          candles, wave incense, chant: "Kakistos... Kakistos..."

                              KAKISTOS
                    Mister Trick...

          Mr. Trick moves brusquely through them to Kakistos.

                              KAKISTOS (cont'd)
                    Talk to me.

                                                         CONTINUED

20 CONTINUED: 20

                              MR. TRICK
                    Check it out. This town -- this very
                    street -- wired for fiber optics. We
                    jack in a T-3, 2500 megs per, we got
                    the whole world at our fingertips.
                              (waves away vamp with
                               incense censer)
                    Theo, allergies.
                              (to Kakistos)
                    What I'm sayin' is, we stay local --
                    where the humans are jumpin' and the
                    cotton is high -- but we live global:
                    you got a hankering for the blood of
                    a fifteen year old Filipina? I'm on
                    the net, she's here the next day,
                    express air.

                              KAKISTOS
                    I want the blood of the Slayer.

                              MR. TRICK
                    On that front, good news and bad --
                    rumor is this town already has a
                    slayer, which makes two, I'm not sure
                    how that happens --

                              KAKISTOS
                              (furious)
                    I don't care if there's a **hundred
                    slayers!!**

Kakistos moves into the dim light. For the first time we get
a look at his face. Not a pretty face. One eye is milky and
useless; a wide-ass scar runs through that eye and down his
terrible face, as if someone parked an axe in it. Even the
unflappable Mr. Trick is flapped. He takes a step back.

                              KAKISTOS (cont'd)
                    I'll kill them all! SHE'S GOING TO
                    PAY FOR WHAT SHE DID TO ME!

Kakistos points to his beastly face with his beastly hand.

                              MR. TRICK
                    Yes she is. I'm running a computer
                    check on every hotel, rooming house
                    and youth hostel in town.

There's a KNOCK at the door. Mr. Trick slips on a long,
radiation-type glove-mitt as:

                                                            CONTINUED

20   CONTINUED: (2)   20

                              MR. TRICK (cont'd)
                    Meanwhile, soon as the sun's down --
                              (re: vamps)
                    -- we're out in force.

Another KNOCK. Trick opens the door. Bright sun surrounds the
squinting:

                              PIZZA GUY
                    You guys order a --

Trick's oven-mitted arm shoots out into the harsh light,
grabs the pizza guy by throat. As he is yanked inside,

21   INT. BUFFY'S HOUSE - DINING ROOM - NIGHT   21

Joyce smiles into CAMERA.

                              JOYCE
                    So you're a slayer, too.

ANGLE - Joyce is piling Faith's plate with food. Buffy sits
nearby, her own plate empty.

                              JOYCE (cont'd)
                    Isn't that interesting. Do you like
                    it?

                              FAITH
                    I love it.

                              BUFFY
                              (gestures with her
                              own empty plate)
                    Mom...

                              JOYCE
                    Just a sec, honey.
                              (to Faith)
                    Buffy never talks that way, why do
                    you love it?

                              FAITH
                    When I'm fighting, the whole world
                    goes away and I only know one thing:
                    I'm gonna win and they're gonna lose.
                    I like that feeling.

Buffy finally starts dishing up her own supper as:

                                                              CONTINUED

21 CONTINUED: 21

                         BUFFY
              Well sure, it's better than that dead
              feeling you get when they win and you
              lose.

                         FAITH
              I don't let that kind of negative
              thinking in.

                         JOYCE
              Right, right, that could get you
              hurt. Buffy can be awfully negative
              sometimes.
                   (turns to Buffy)
              See, honey, you gotta fight that.

                         BUFFY
              I'm trying.

                         JOYCE
              Faith, can I get you another soft
              drink?

                         FAITH
              You bet, thanks.

Joyce heads for the kitchen.

                         FAITH (cont'd)
              She's cool.

                         BUFFY
              Best mom ever. Excuse me.

Buffy heads for the:

22 INT. BUFFY'S HOUSE - KITCHEN/DINING ROOM - NIGHT   22

As Joyce re-fills Faith's soda.

                         JOYCE
              I like this girl, Buffy.

                         BUFFY
              Yeah, she's personable. Gets along
              with my friends, my watcher, my
              mom -- look! Now she's getting along
              with my fries!

CONTINUED

22   CONTINUED: 22

ANGLE: FAITH is in fact reaching over and snagging some of
Buffy's fries.

                    JOYCE
          Now, Buffy --

                    BUFFY
          Plus, in school today, she was making
          eyes at MY not-boyfriend. It's
          creepy.

                    JOYCE
          Does anybody else think Faith is
          creepy?

                    BUFFY
          No, but I'm the one getting Single
          White Femaled here.

                    JOYCE
          It's probably good you were an only
          child.

                    BUFFY
          Hey, I... Mom, I'm just getting my
          life back. I'm not looking to go
          halfsies on it.

                    JOYCE
          Well, there are some things I'd be
          happy to see you share. Like the
          Slaying. Two of you fighting is
          safer than one, right?

                    BUFFY
          Yeah, I guess...

                    JOYCE
          Unless -- you heard her, she loves
          the slaying, couldn't she take over
          for you?

                    BUFFY
          No one can take over for me, Mom.

                    JOYCE
          But next year you'll be in college,
          I don't see why --

                                              CONTINUED

22   CONTINUED: (2)   22

                         BUFFY
              The only way you get a new slayer is
              when the old one dies.

                         JOYCE
              That means you... when did you die,
              you never told me you died!

                         BUFFY
              ...it was just for a few minutes.

                         JOYCE
              I hate this, I hate your life.

                         BUFFY
              Mom...

                         JOYCE
              I know you didn't choose this, I know
              it chose you... I've tried to march
              in the slayer pride parade but...
                    (weakly)
              ...I don't want you to die.

         Buffy hugs her mom.

                         BUFFY
              It's okay, I'm not going to die. I
              know how to do this job, besides,
              like you said, I've got help now.

         Buffy indicates Faith in the dining room. Joyce nods.

                         BUFFY (cont'd)
              I've got all the help I can stand.

                                                              *

23   EXT. SUNNYDALE STREETS/CONSTRUCTION SITE - NIGHT   23

         Buffy and Faith patrol. They move in silence for a beat, then:

                         FAITH
              Didn't we already do this street?

                         BUFFY
              Weird thing about vampires, they'll
              hit a place even after you've been
              there. It's like they have no manners.

                                                    CONTINUED

23 CONTINUED: 23

                        FAITH
                    (shrugs)
              You're the one who's been doing this
              the longest.

                        BUFFY
              I have.

                        FAITH
              ...maybe too long ...

                        BUFFY
              What's that supposed to mean?

                        FAITH
              Nothing.

                        BUFFY
              You got a problem?

                        FAITH
              I'm five by five, B. Living entirely
              large and wondering 'bout **your**
              problem.

                        BUFFY
              I may not sleep in the nude and
              wrestle alligators --

                        FAITH
              Well maybe it's time you started.
              Something in your bottle needs
              uncorking. Is it this Angel thing?

                        BUFFY
              What do you know about Angel?

                        FAITH
              What your friends tell me: big love,
              big loss, you oughta deal and move on
              but you're not.

Buffy stops, gets in Faith's face.

                        BUFFY
              I got an idea: how 'bout from now on
              we don't hear from you on Angel or
              anything else in my life. Which by
              way, is **my** life.

                                                        CONTINUED

23   CONTINUED: (2)   23

                              FAITH
                    What are you getting so strung out
                    for, B?

                              BUFFY
                    Why are your lips still moving, "F"?

                              FAITH
                    Did I just hear a threat?

                              BUFFY
                    Would you like to?

                              FAITH
                         (beat)
                    Wow. Think you can take me?

                              BUFFY
                    Yeah --
                         (sees something O.S.)
                    I just hope they can't.

And Buffy suddenly shoves Faith hard -- and out of the way --
stakes our CONTEST WINNING VAMP as Vamps 2, 3, & 4 attack!   *

Buffy punches 2, sidesteps an onslaught from 3 and spin kicks
4 -- who blocks the kick and smashes her in the face. Buffy
stumbles back, momentarily stunned.

Faith gets her wits, barrels at 4. She hits him hard in the
mid-section and they crash back into the wall.

Buffy punches and kicks 3 as 2 grabs a two by four from the
building sight and wallops her with it. Buffy goes down.

Faith and 4 trade punches.

                              FAITH
                    Come on! My dead mother hits harder
                    than that!

Buffy looks up from the ground, rolls as the two by four
misses her face by inches, sweeps 3's legs out from under
him, wrenches the two by four out of 2's hands and gut
punches 2 with it. She glances over at:

FAITH - crazed, knocks 4 to the ground, leaps on him,
punching the shit out of him.

                                                          CONTINUED

23 CONTINUED: (3)   23

                         FAITH (cont'd)
             YEAH, THIS IS ME, YOU UNDEAD BASTARD!

                         BUFFY
             Faith! You want to stake him already
             and give me a hand?

But Faith is in her own rage-filled world, as 3 leaps on
Buffy from behind and 2 punches her in the side of the head.
Buffy falls to the ground, 2 and 3 on her, each pinning a
shoulder to the ground.

3 bends down to bite her neck.

                         VAMP
             For Kakistos we live... for Kakistos,
             you die.

                         BUFFY
         FAITH!

Off Faith, oblivious to Buffy and everything else, hitting
the vamp over and over..

                                        BLACK OUT.

                    END OF ACT TWO

ACT THREE

24 EXT. CONSTRUCTION SITE - NIGHT   24   *

As before. Faith beating on 4, Buffy about to get bit.

Buffy slides the two by four out from under her, jams it
under a fence bracket and jerks up on it, breaking it in two
and smashing 3 in the face with it at the same time. She
rolls onto her back, staking 2 to dust with the shardy end,
and flips to her feet.

Buffy back-stakes 3 without even looking and marches to:

FAITH - punching away at 4, angry and incoherent.

                    FAITH
          You... can't... touch... me...!

BUFFY - yanks Faith off the unconscious vamp with one hand,
stakes the vamp with her other. Then she turns to Faith who
is breathing hard, high on adrenaline, rubbing her fists.

                    BUFFY
          What is wrong with you?

                    FAITH
          What are you talking about?

                    BUFFY
          I'm talking about you living large on
          the great undead here.

                    FAITH
          Gee, if doing violence to vampires
          upsets you, I'm pretty sure you're in
          the wrong line a work...

                    BUFFY
          Or maybe you like it just a little
          too much.

                    FAITH
          I was getting the job done.

                    BUFFY
          The job is to slay demons. Not mash
          'em into sloppy joes while their
          friends are cornering me.

CONTINUED

24   CONTINUED: 24

                         FAITH
              I thought you could handle yourself.

Off Buffy,

25   INT. SCHOOL HALL - DAY   25

Buffy walks with Giles.

                         GILES
              Well, Buffy, you have to realize you
              and Faith have very different
              temperaments...

                         BUFFY
              I know, mine would be the sane one.
              Giles, she's not playing with a full
              deck. She has almost no deck. She
              has a three.

                         GILES
              You said yourself she killed one of
              them, she's a plucky fighter who got
              a little carried away. Which is
              natural, she's focussed on Slaying,
              she doesn't have a whole other life
              here like you --

                         BUFFY
              -- she doesn't need a whole other
              life here, she's got mine.

                         GILES
              I think you're being a little...

                         BUFFY
              No, I'm being a lot. I know that. But
              I'm telling you, she nearly got us
              both killed, she needs help.

                         GILES
              I'll see if I can get word to her
              watcher at the retreat...
                         (checks watch)
              Eight hours later, they're probably
              enjoying a nightcap... I wonder if
              they still kayak.
                         (more)

                                                          CONTINUED

25 CONTINUED: 25

                        GILES (cont'd)
            I was an excellent kayaker in my day,
            do they even consider that...?
                    (off her look)
            Sorry. Now these vampires that
            attacked you, did you notice any
            details that might help me trace
            their lineage: modern or ancient
            dress, amulets, cultish tattoos...?

                        BUFFY
            No tats, crappy dressers, oh, the one
            who nearly bit me said something
            about... kissing toast, he lived for
            kissing toast.

                        GILES
                    (alarmed)
            You mean Kakistos?

                        BUFFY
                    (still thinking)
            Or, it could have been taquitos,
            maybe he lived for taquitos... what'd
            you say?

                        GILES
            Kakistos.

Giles heads into the library with purpose. She follows:

                        BUFFY
            Is that bad?

26 INT. LIBRARY - DAY   26

                        GILES
            Kakistos is Greek, it means the worst   *
            of the worst. It's also the name of   *
            a vampire, so old his hands and feet   *
            are cloven. He must be here for some   *
            reason.

                        BUFFY
            This guys shows up when, two days ago?
            Right around the time my bestest new
            little sister makes the scene.

                                                        CONTINUED

26 CONTINUED: 26

                        GILES
              You think Faith is connected to
              Kakistos somehow?

                                                              *

                        BUFFY
              There's two things I do not believe
              in. Coincidence and leprechauns.

                        GILES
              Buffy, it's entirely possible they
              happened by chance to arrive
              simultaneously.

                        BUFFY
              Okay, but I'm right about
              leprechauns, right?

                        GILES
              As far as I know.

                        BUFFY
              Good. Get England on the phone. I'm   *
              gonna talk to Faith. See if Kakistos
              rings a bell. Or an alarm.

        Buffy heads out.

27 INT. HALL NEAR SCHOOL LOUNGE - DAY   27

        Buffy heads for the exit, runs into:

                        SCOTT
              Hi.

                        BUFFY
              Scott...

                        SCOTT
              How are you?

                        BUFFY
              Okay. I've gotta...

                        SCOTT
              I know, be somewhere else. Think of
              this as my last ditch effort, I
              realize one more will qualify as
              stalking.
                        (more)

                                                    CONTINUED

27   CONTINUED: 27

                         SCOTT (cont'd)
                           (beat)
                    I've given a lot of thought, some
                    might say too much thought, to how I
                    might be a part of your life. It
                    begins with conversation, we all know
                    this. Maybe over a cup of coffee,
                    maybe at the Buster Keaton
                    festival -- playing on State Street
                    all this weekend.

Beat.

                         BUFFY
                    Looking back now I see I haven't
                    really been fair to... Buster Keaton.
                    I like what I've seen of him so far,
                    I think it's time to see a little
                    more.

                         SCOTT
                           (success at last)
                    Keaton is key.

Giles, looking concerned, hurries down the hall towards Buffy
in b.g, approaching in time to witness:

                         SCOTT (cont'd)
                           (pulling out a small
                           white box)
                    I got you a little present, guy in a
                    retro shop said it represents
                    friendship -- that's something I'd
                    very much like to have with you.

Buffy smiles, he's charmed and relaxed her. Scott hands her
the box. She looks in, her smile fades.

IN THE BOX - a Claddagh ring, just like the one Angel gave
her.

                         SCOTT (O.S.)
                    You like?

Buffy steps back (towards Giles), dropping the box. The ring
clatters to the floor, much like it did in her dream.

FLASHCUT: Angel putting the ring on her finger in episode 13,
year 2.

                                                        CONTINUED

27   CONTINUED: (2)   27

BACK IN PRESENT

Scott picks up the ring as:

                    BUFFY
          I can't... I can't do this...

ANGLE - THE RING IN SCOTT'S HAND

Is not the Claddagh ring but a simple friendship ring,
colored plastic or something markedly different.

                    SCOTT
          Okay, I get the message.

Buffy turns, walks into Giles (Scott exiting in b.g.)

                    GILES
          Are you all right?

                    BUFFY
          Yeah. I'm fine. Did you reach the
          retreat?

                    GILES
          I did.

                    BUFFY
          What'd her watcher say?

                    GILES
          Her watcher is dead.

28   EXT. CHEESY MOTEL - NIGHT - ESTABLISHING   28   *

29   INT. CHEESY MOTEL ROOM - NIGHT   29   *

The door to the hall is open. Faith faces the hefty MANAGER.   *

                    MANAGER
          Room's eighteen dollars a day, that's
          every day.

                    FAITH
          I know. I'll get it to you tomorrow,
          I swear.

                                                   CONTINUED

29 CONTINUED: 29

                          MANAGER
                It's not like I own the place.

                          FAITH
                     (sexy)
                Bet you will someday.

                          MANAGER
                Not if I listen to broads like you.

He turns to go. Buffy is standing in the doorway.

                          MANAGER (cont'd)
                Roommates are extra.

                          BUFFY
                Just visiting.

Manager gives her a look. Buffy shuts the door.

                          FAITH
                What brings you to the po' side of
                town?

                          BUFFY
                Cloven guy, goes by the name of
                Kakistos.

Faith goes very cold and hard.

                          FAITH
                ...what do you know about Kakistos?

                          BUFFY
                That he's here.

Faith just stares.

                          BUFFY (cont'd)
                So we're not happy to see old
                friends. What'd he do to you?

                          FAITH
                It's what I did to him...

She grabs a bag, starts throwing her few belongings in.

                                                      CONTINUED

29 CONTINUED: (2)   29

                        BUFFY
          What would that be?
                    (nothing from Faith)
          You came here for a reason, Faith, I
          can help --

                        FAITH
          You can mind your own business. I'm
          the one can handle this.

                        BUFFY
          Yeah, you're a real badass when it
          comes to packing. What'd you say
          about my problem, gotta deal and move
          on...?

Faith picks up her bag, turns to face Buffy.

                        BUFFY (cont'd)
          Here we have the moving on part, I
          get that -- and dealing, that's
          something you just gonna dump on my
          doorstep?

                        FAITH
          You don't know me, you don't know
          what I've been through. I'll take
          care of it.

She heads for the door.

                        BUFFY
          Like you took care of your watcher?

Faith stops.

                        BUFFY (cont'd)
          He killed her, didn't he?

Faith looks back at Buffy, dropping the tough girl act:

                        FAITH
          They don't have a word for what he
          did to her.

Then she reaches for the door -- someone KNOCKS, scaring the
hell out of her. She looks through the peephole.

PEEPHOLE CAM - A fishy view of the Manager.

                                                       CONTINUED

29 CONTINUED: (3)   29

                    FAITH (cont'd)
          What now...

                    BUFFY
          Faith, you run, he runs after.

                    FAITH
          Yeah, that's where the head start
          comes in so handy.

Faith opens the door. The manager teeters there, just as dead
as a man can be. Kakistos stands behind him, holding his neck.

Faith goes stone cold with fear. Mr. Trick (in vampface here
and throughout the rest of the script) and Vamp 5 flank
Kakistos who lets go of the manager's neck. The manager falls
to the floor.

                    KAKISTOS
          Faith...

                              BLACK OUT.

          END OF ACT THREE

ACT FOUR

30   INT. CHEESY MOTEL ROOM - NIGHT   30

Kakistos reaches out and grabs Faith. Buffy runs at the door,   *
hits it with her shoulder, slamming it on Kakistos' arm,   *
ramming it against the door jam. His hand holds fast to
Faith's neck. Buffy whips out a stake, stabs Kakistos'   *
forearm. We HEAR Kakistos howl in pain, he lets go of Faith's   *
neck.

Buffy stabs it some more, driving it back -- she slams and
locks the door. Faith is just crazy with fear.

                    FAITH
          No... no...

                    BUFFY
          It's okay, I just bought us a
          little --

Kakistos' fish comes smashing through the door, nearly taking   *
Faith's head off.

                    BUFFY (cont'd)
          -- time.

Faith starts screaming. Buffy slaps her hard across the face.

                    BUFFY (cont'd)
          Scream later, escape now.

Buffy races to the window -- sees Vamps 6 & 7 posted outside.
Meanwhile, the motel door is being ripped off its hinges by
Kakistos.
                                                                 *
Buffy picks up a chair and hurls it through the window,
knocking the two vamps outside down. Buffy grabs Faith:

                    BUFFY (cont'd)
          Go!

They jump out the window (Buffy elbow-smashes Vamp 6 who is
getting to his feet) as Kakistos, Trick and Vamp 5 bust into
the room and run for the window --   *

31   EXT. CHEESY MOTEL - NIGHT   31

Buffy and Faith run for it.

32   EXT. STREET - NIGHT   32

Kakistos, Trick, three vamps run after.   *

BUFFY AND FAITH - running like hell. Buffy grabs Faith, they veer off the street, vault a hedge or low fence, cutting through a property.

KAKISTOS, TRICK AND THE OTHERS

Mr. Trick points down the street: Vamps 6 & 7 keep going straight; Kakistos leaps the hedge, following Buffy and Faith directly; Mr. Trick and Vamp 5 cut hard right -- splitting into three different flanks now. [**Note:** How 'bout a big-ass aerial shot of them splitting off in three different directions, I'm just sayin'.]

33   EXT. ANOTHER STREET - NIGHT   33

Faith and Buffy burst into the street, see:

THE TWO VAMPS

Rounding a corner.

BUFFY AND FAITH

Run the other way, see:

TRICK AND THE OTHER VAMP

Coming from that direction.

BUFFY AND FAITH

Tear down an alley, turn a corner. A few feet from the corner, an abandoned firehouse.

34   INT. ABANDONED FIREHOUSE - NIGHT   34

Buffy and Faith tumble through a half broken window, hit the floor. Buffy jumps up, looks out the window.

BUFFY'S POV

Kakistos runs across the "T" in the alley, missing the turn Buffy and Faith took.

                              BUFFY
                    We're okay.

                                                      CONTINUED

34 CONTINUED: 34

Faith glances out of the window herself, badly shaken.

                    BUFFY (cont'd)
          What happened?

                    FAITH
          I...
               (starts to cry)

                    BUFFY
          It's okay.

                    FAITH
          I was there when he killed my
          watcher. I saw what he did to her,
          what he was going to do to me... I
          tried to stop him, but I couldn't...
          I ran...

                    BUFFY
          Faith, listen to me. First rule of
          slaying: don't die. You did the right
          thing, you didn't die. Now do the
          math: one of him, two of us...

                    FAITH
               (softly)
          No...

                    BUFFY
          Yes.

                    FAITH
               (terror-stricken)
          No...

Buffy follows her gaze. In the corner, a gruesome pile of
bodies. Happy Burger guy, Pizza Guy, a couple of other
uniformed corpses, Meter Reader, Mail Woman, etc.

                    FAITH (cont'd)
          This is his place.

Buffy spins around: Trick and Vamp 5 coming through a back
entrance, Kakistos coming through the side, Vamps 6 & 7   *
behind him. They're surrounded and, need I mention, badly out-
numbered.   *

                                                      CONTINUED

34 CONTINUED: (2)   34

                         BUFFY
                       (realizing)
                They drove us here.

Here come the vamps. Buffy kicks vamp 5 in the face, punches
6.

Faith can't take her eyes off Kakistos; she backs away in   *
terror.

Buffy sees this, grabs a metal bar.

                    BUFFY (cont'd)
                <u>Don't die</u>.

Buffy hurls the metal bar into Faith's arms.

Buffy whips out a stake, diving for Kakistos who catches her   *
with one hand -- and hurls her against a wall.

Faith looks at the bar in her hands, up at Kakistos. She is   *
not doing well here. She tries to swing it -- Kakistos stops   *
it and punches her <u>right through</u> a support beam.

BUFFY - On her back on the floor; Vamp 5 dives for her. She
whips out a stake.

ANGLE - THE WALL ABOVE BUFFY AND VAMP 5.

We see 5's dust cloud as Buffy pops up to her feet out of it,
stake in hand; she spins to see:

ANGLE: FAITH

crawling painfully away from where she landed, Kakistos   *
moving towards her.

Buffy is about to go for Kakistos when Mister Trick (in   *
vampface) grabs her from behind.

                    MR. TRICK
                I believe this dance is mine.

She slams him back against the wall, bends forward and flips
him over into his back, whips out her stake --

                    BUFFY
                The music stopped.

                                                        CONTINUED

34 CONTINUED: (3)   34

She drives the stake down -- but he rolls away, comes back up
to face her.

                    MR. TRICK
          But the beat goes on. Gimmie
          whatchya got.

She comes at him, and they trade just enough punches so we
know they're a good match.

KAKISTOS TOWERS OVER

Faith. Grabs her hair, drags her to her feet. She looks at
him beyond terror now...

BUFFY AND TRICK

Going at it as Vamp 6 grabs Buffy from behind. Trick comes
for her, she rears back, kicks him in the face, flips 6 over
her shoulder and stakes him (out of C.G.I. sight) on the
ground. Buffy sees:

KAKISTOS HIT FAITH REALLY HARD

She's down and out, folks.

BUFFY RUNS LIKE HELL

Diving, hitting Kakistos in the mid-section, she starts
raining kicks and blows upon him.

Vampire 7 rises, Mr. Trick stepping up next to her.   *

                    MR. TRICK (cont'd)
                    (urgently)   *
          We don't do something fast, the   *
          master could be killed.   *

A beat.   *

                    MR. TRICK (cont'd)   *
          Well, our prayers are with him.

He turns to go, the other vampire going with him, a tad   *
reluctantly.   *

                                                   CONTINUED

34   CONTINUED: (4)   34

                         MR. TRICK (cont'd)
                There's a reason why these vengeance   *
                crusades are out of style. The   *
                modern vampire looks at the big   *
                picture....   *

                                                    CONTINUED

34   CONTINUED: (4)   34

ANGLE - OVER BUFFY AND KAKISTOS   *

Trick and Vamp 7 slip out the door as Buffy comes up with a
stake, ducks a giant swing from Kakistos and sinks the stake   *
deep and true into his chest.

Nothing happens.

Buffy pounds on the stake, trying to sink it deeper. Still
nothing -- and now Kakistos starts laughing.   *

                    KAKISTOS
          Guess you need a bigger stake, slayer.

WIDER

Kakistos is still laughing as Faith rises from the ashes, the   *
broken support beam in hand. He just has time to register
this as she rams it through his chest. Oh yeah, he's dust now.

BUFFY AND FAITH

Stand there, breathing hard, looking around: the others are
gone, it's over. They look at each other.

                    BUFFY
          You hungry?

                    FAITH
          Starved.

As they walk,

35   EXT. SUNNYDALE HIGH - DAY - ESTABLISHING   35

36   INT. LIBRARY - DAY   36

Buffy is with Giles and Willow.

                    GILES
          The Council approved our request,
          Faith can stay here indefinitely, I'm
          to look after you both until they
          assign a new watcher.

                                              CONTINUED

36 CONTINUED: 36

>   BUFFY
>   Good. She came through, you know.
>   She had a lot to deal with, but she
>   did it. Got it behind her.

>   GILES
>   That's good to hear.

A moment, as Buffy looks down, gathers something in herself.

>   BUFFY
>   Angel was cured.

>   GILES
>   I'm sorry?

>   BUFFY
>   When I killed him, Angel was...
>   cured. Your spell worked, Willow.
>   Last minute. I was about to take him
>   and then he was... Angel again. He
>   didn't remember anything he'd done,
>   he just held me, and...
>   (this is tough)
>   ...but it was, it was too late and
>   I had to... I kissed him, and I told
>   him that I loved him. And I killed
>   him.

There is a long silence. Buffy looks at her friends,
maintaining surprisingly well.

>   BUFFY (cont'd)
>   I don't know if that helps with your
>   spell or not, Giles.

>   GILES
>   I believe it will.

>   WILLOW
>   I'm sorry...

>   BUFFY
>   It's okay. I guess I been holding
>   onto that. It's actually kinda good
>   to get it out.
>   (picks up her books)
>   I'll see you guys later.

CONTINUED

36   CONTINUED: (2)   36

    Giles nods. Buffy goes. Beat. Giles begins gathering up some
    of his herbs and talismans.

                    WILLOW
        Giles? I know you don't like me
        playing with the mystical forces, but
        I really could help with the binding
        spell.

                    GILES
        There is no spell.

    A moment, as Willow gets it. Giles looks a moment more
    towards the door, then heads into his office.

37   INT. SCHOOL - DAY   37   *

    Between classes. Scott exits a class. Rounds a corner, finds:

                    BUFFY
        Hi.

                    SCOTT
        Hello.

                    BUFFY
        So I was just... waiting here for you
        to get out of your class.

                    SCOTT
        Why?

                    BUFFY
        I'm really sorry about going mental
        on you... there was someone a while
        ago and the ring sort of confused me
        but... I liked what you said about
        friendship, I liked it a lot. Also,
        Buster Keaton, big fun. And I'm
        capable of the big fun even though
        there's no earthly way you could
        possibly know that about me lately.
        Wow, if I'd known I was going to go
        on this long I'd have brought water.
        So, if you were still up for the film
        festival -- and I'd understand if you
        weren't -- I'd pretty much love to go
        with you.

                                                    CONTINUED

37 CONTINUED: 37

                      SCOTT
         I don't know, Buffy. I'm really gonna
         have to think this over.

He turns, walks away. She barely has time to deflate before
he turns and comes right back.

                  SCOTT (cont'd)
         Okay, thought it over. I'm in. When
         do you want to go?

                    BUFFY
          (smiles, then:)
         I have one thing I have to do
         tonight, after that I'm good.

                  SCOTT
         Good.

Off them,

38 EXT. MANSION - NIGHT - ESTABLISHING   38

39 INT. MANSION - NIGHT   39

Buffy enters, moves through the darkened room, remembering.
She walks to where she stabbed Angel. Looks down at the
Claddagh ring in her hand.

She closes her hand around the ring, kneels down, where Angel
was cast into hell. Holding the ring tightly. Then:

                    BUFFY
         Goodbye.

She opens her hand, let's go of the ring. It slips to the
ground (again, not unlike in her dream?) She stays there very
still as if in prayer.

BIG INSERT - THE RING

comes to rest on the ground.

BUFFY RISES

She's not dancing and singing, but she's taken the first step
in the long journey that will put him to rest and allow her
to get on with her life.

CONTINUED

39 CONTINUED: 39

She turns and walks out the front door.

HOLD THE ROOM

As our music gently builds to the end and the scene starts to
fade. It fades to black, until the only thing visible in the
room is the ring itself.

Visible because we now realize: it's glowing.

And then there's a LOW RUMBLING TREMOR which builds to a
frightening crescendo culminating in --

A BLINDING FLASH OF LIGHTS

Something DARK AND LARGE hurtles out of the lights and lands
on the cold stone floor. PUSH IN:

Naked and shivering, virtually mad, something huddles
there -- something fresh out of hell -- his own hand inches
away from the ring: Angel.

                                        BLACK OUT.

            THE END

BUFFY THE VAMPIRE SLAYER

"Beauty and the Beasts"

Written By

Marti Noxon

Directed By

James Whitmore Jr.

<u>SHOOTING SCRIPT</u>

August 19, 1998 (WHITE)

BUFFY THE VAMPIRE SLAYER

"Beauty and the Beasts"

CAST LIST

BUFFY SUMMERS......................... Sarah Michelle Gellar
XANDER HARRIS......................... Nicholas Brendon
RUPERT GILES......................... Anthony S. Head
WILLOW ROSENBERG...................... Alyson Hannigan
CORDELIA CHASE....................... Charisma Carpenter
ANGEL................................ David Boreanaz
OZ................................... Seth Green

FAITH..................................* Eliza Dushku
SCOTT..................................* Fab Filippo
DEBBIE.................................* Danielle Weeks
PETE...................................* John Patrick White
MR. PLATT..............................* Phill Lewis

BUFFY THE VAMPIRE SLAYER

"Beauty and the Beasts"

SET LIST

INTERIORS

SUNNYDALE HIGH SCHOOL
    LIBRARY
    HALLWAY
    ANOTHER PART OF THE HALLWAY
    COUNSELOR'S OFFICE
    CAFETERIA
    GARDEN SHED
    GIRL'S LOCKER ROOM

MORGUE

MANSION

EXTERIORS

SUNNYDALE HIGH SCHOOL
 FOUNTAIN COURTYARD
 SCHOOL GROUNDS

CEMETERY

WOODS

BUFFY THE VAMPIRE SLAYER

"Beauty and the Beasts"

TEASER

1 EXT. WOODS - NIGHT   1

Shadowy and overgrown. Dream-like. Through the tangle of
bushes and trees - something runs through the night woods.
A snarling creature, obscured by darkness. Over this we hear-

                    BUFFY (V.O.)
          "One night, after supper, the lead
          dog turned up a shoeshoe rabbit. The
          dog lay down low to the race, his
          body flashing forward, leap by
          leap... He was sounding the deeps of
          his nature, and the parts of his
          nature that were deeper than he -
          going back into the wombs of time..."

Now Buffy's voice MELDS into WILLOW'S as we-

                                        FADE TO:

2 INT. LIBRARY - NIGHT   2

And find Willow, trying to stay awake, as she walks in front
of the book cage, reading aloud from Jack London's "Call of
the Wild." A CLOCK ON THE WALL nearby reads 3:17 AM.

                    WILLOW
                  (reading)
          "...going back into the wombs of
          time. The rabbit could not turn-"

Now she is STARTLED by OZ, in full wolf mode, as HE LEAPS
into frame behind her - slamming into the cage. If Oz
understands her, he gives no indication - just starts pacing
the cage, restless.

                    WILLOW (cont'd)
          Maybe we should pick a less -
          stimulating - passage...

She starts to leaf through the book when XANDER enters,
looking less than fully awake. He carries a thermos and some
magazines.

                    XANDER
          Private Harris reporting for Oz watch.

                                        CONTINUED

                    177

2 CONTINUED: 2

                          WILLOW
                Xander - oh good...

She moves to him - hands him the book.

                          XANDER
                "Call of the Wild." Aren't we
                reading the Cliff Notes to this for
                English?

                          WILLOW
                     (gives him a look)
                Some of us are. Anyway, it'll help
                you stay awake. It's good and very
                wolfy. And it seems to sooth the
                savage beast. Except the stuff
                about...
                     (glances at Oz/low
                      whisper)
                Rabbits.

Xander looks through the book - confused.

                          XANDER
                Rabbis?

                          WILLOW
                He gets sort of... over excited.
                     (baby-sitter talk)
                Now. He's already had his two
                o'clock feeding. After sunrise, if
                he forgets where his clothes are -
                they're on top of the file cabinet in
                his cage. And I put that towel up
                for privacy.

We see that, indeed, there is a towel pinned up in the cage.

                          XANDER
                No worries. I can handle the Oz full
                monty.
                     (quickly)
                I mean - not handle, handle - like
                "hands to flesh" handle.

                          WILLOW
                It's not you I'm worried about. It's
                me. I'm still getting used to half
                a monty.

                                                    CONTINUED

2   CONTINUED: (2)   2

                              XANDER
                    Oh, good -
                         (alarmed)
                    Half? You and Oz? Which half?

                              WILLOW
                         (enjoying his wiggins)
                    Wouldn't you like to know.
                         (moving on)
                    Okay - he's more manageable tonight
                    and on night three. Tomorrow - the
                    total full moon? That's the real
                    howler. Still, if there's trouble -
                    there won't be - but, you know, <u>if</u>...

Willow hands Xander a BIG ASS TRANQUILIZER GUN.

                              XANDER
                    Sleepy time. Gotchya.

Now she grabs her stuff. Heads for the door.

                              WILLOW
                    Thanks again for doing this. I
                    wouldn't ask but I have this test-

                              XANDER
                    No big. You can count on me. I got
                    my coffee, magazines... Figured I'd
                    read, run the stairs here... I'm good.

Willow waves and is off. Xander moves to the cage - checks
the door. It's secure. Then he sits at the table,
contemplates reading to Oz - but instead tosses the book
aside and lays his head down...

3   EXT. CEMETARY - NIGHT   3

Buffy and Faith patrol together. The park is quiet, and they
enjoy a rare moment of girl bonding.

                              FAITH
                    You ever catch kids doing the
                    horizontal two-step out here?

                              BUFFY
                    Naw. There's a smooch spot near the
                    woods. That's where folks go.

                              FAITH
                    Yeah? Bet you and Scott been out
                    there kicking the old gearshift.

                                                        CONTINUED

3 CONTINUED: 3

                           BUFFY
              Hardly. We've only been out a few
              times.

                           FAITH
              But you like him, right? When you
              think about him you get that good,
              down low tickle?

                           BUFFY
              Well, yeah.
                      (then)
              How low?

                           FAITH
                      (grins)
              You tell me.

                           BUFFY
              How 'bout - not?
                      (then)
              But he is funny and nice and-

                           FAITH
              -quite a muffin.

                           BUFFY
              Blueberry. With that munchable,
              crumbly top. But my most favorite
              thing? So far, he doesn't seem to be
              some sort of hell beast.

                           FAITH
              All men are beasts, Buffy.

                           BUFFY
              Geez. I was sort of hoping not to
              sound that cynical until at least
              forty.

                           FAITH
              Not cynical. Realistic. Every
              guy - from "Manimal" right on down to
              "Mr. I Loved The English Patient"
              - has beast in him. And I don't care
              how sensitive they act -- they're
              still just in it for the chase...

4 EXT. WOODS - NIGHT   4

    Speaking of.... We hear the RASPY, GUTTERAL BREATHING of
    something INHUMAN as it pursues a TERRIFIED YOUNG MAN through
    the woods.

    The kid's clothes are torn and bloodied, his face and body
    horribly scratched. He stumbles, hits the ground hard and
    scrambles to regain his footing. But the creature pursuing
    him, still UNSEEN (except, perhaps, in quick flashes of an
    UNCLEAR BEAST/MAN SILHOUETTE) GRABS HIM BY HIS LEGS - yanking
    him out of frame and to a hideous (off camera) bone-crushing,
    flesh-tearing fate.

                            BLACK OUT.

                    END OF TEASER

ACT ONE

5   EXT. FOUNTAIN COURTYARD - DAY   5

Buffy, Willow and Oz walk toward school, in mid-talk.

                    WILLOW
                  (worried)
            I don't think that's true. That
            every guy is in it for the chase.

                    BUFFY
            I know, it's awfully-

                    SCOTT (O.C.)
            Buffy! Wait up!

Now we see SCOTT - who runs to catch up with her, leaving his
buddy, PETE, and Pete's girlfriend, DEBBIE, behind.

                    SCOTT
            Hey.
                  (off her questioning
                   look)
            That's what I stopped you for,
            basically. Hey.

                    BUFFY
                  (pleased)
            Okay. Hey.

Pete and Debbie also come over - but at a less infatuated
pace. Pete's an attractive, friendly guy. Debbie is cute
but also a little withdrawn.

Oz nods to Debbie - he knows her.

                    OZ
            Howdy Debbie.

                    DEBBIE
            Hi, Oz. Hey, you're not doing Jazz
            band this year?

                    OZ
            Can't take the pressure. It's not
            the music that's hard, it's the
            marching.

                    BUFFY
            We have a marching Jazz band?

                                            CONTINUED

5   CONTINUED: 5

                         OZ
          Yeah. But - you know - good jazz is
          improvisational. So we'd be marching
          off in all directions. Running into
          floats and stuff. Scary.

                         WILLOW
          He's just being Oz.

                         OZ
          Pretty much full time.

Buffy notices that Debbie is holding a small bouquet of wild
flowers.

                         BUFFY
          Those are pretty.

Debbie beams happily.

                         DEBBIE
          Thanks. Pete brought them for me.

                         PETE
               (embarrassed)
          It's... Well, you know. I'm sure
          Scott does that kind of stuff for you
          too, Buffy.

                         SCOTT
          Oh. We're not up to flowers.
               (suddenly anxious)
          Are we? Up to flowers? Did I miss
          flowers?

                         BUFFY
          No. We're pre-posie. Definitely.
               (checks her watch; to
                Scott)
          I'd better go. Lucky me, I get to
          see Mr. Platt today.

Debbie makes a face. Yuck.

                         DEBBIE
          Platt? The school counselor?

                         BUFFY
          Yeah - I need to convince him I'm
          "Little Ms. Stable" so I can stay in
          school.

                                              CONTINUED

5   CONTINUED: (2)   5

                              SCOTT
                 Stable. Okay. Topics to avoid. The
                 little men that live in your teeth...
                 Your compulsion to paint circus
                 clowns...

                              BUFFY
                         (sincerely)
                 But if God keeps telling me to
                 kill - it just seems snotty not to,
                 you know?

                              SCOTT
                 You'll do great.

                              DEBBIE
                 Platt creeps me out. I would totally
                 quit going, but I'm flunking senior
                 bio and my teacher says I hate
                 "success issues."

                              OZ
                 Senior Bio? I sort of aced that
                 final.

                              WILLOW
                         (teasing)
                 And how did you do that? Oh,
                 right - you showed up.

                              OZ
                         (to Debbie)
                 You want my notes - they're yours.

                              DEBBIE
                 Thanks. That'd be great.

                              BUFFY
                 See you.

        They start to go off in separate directions. Buffy gives
        Scott a quick kiss on the lips before parting.

                              SCOTT
                 Yeah. Good.

6   INT. SCHOOL - HALLWAY - DAY   6

        Buffy talks to Oz and Willow as they move down the hall.

                              WILLOW
                 Okay. You. Scott. School kiss.

                                                            CONTINUED

6 CONTINUED: 6

                    BUFFY
          Not a deal. We've kissed before.

                    WILLOW
          But in the dark. Alone. A school
          kiss is a whole 'nother deal. It's
          statement-y. It says - hey, peers -
          we're smooching!

                    BUFFY
               (anxious now)
          Do you think it was too much?

                    OZ
          I thought it was right. It said
          "nice seeing you" - not - "take me
          now." Not that I have anything
          against a "take me now" kiss, mind
          you. But it's not very school.

                    WILLOW
          Totally. That kind of kiss in school
          is all about showing off. The
          "haves" rubbing it in the faces of
          the "have-nots."

Now Willow stops at her locker. Oz lingers with her as
Buffy, preoccupied, moves on down the hall.

                    BUFFY
          So I'm good. Yeah. I think...

And she's gone. Willow turns to Oz.

                    WILLOW
          I'm not sure I completely understand.
          What was the first kind of kiss?

                    OZ
          Oh. That would be the "nice seeing
          you kiss."

                    WILLOW
          And - how does that go?

Oz smiles - getting it. He leans in, kisses her sweetly but
quickly.

                                                    CONTINUED

6 CONTINUED: (2)   6

                              OZ
                    Nice seeing you.
                              (then)
                    Of course - it can be a fine line.
                    The "nice to see you" kiss can easily
                    morph into...

Now he gives her a slightly longer, more intense kiss.

                              OZ (cont'd)
                    <u>Really</u> nice seeing you. And if you
                    aren't careful, that becomes...

A pretty intense smooch which shows no signs of stopping. So
intense, in fact, that they don't notice TWO FRESHMAN BOYS
who pass them and roll their eyes. Show offs.

7 INT. LIBRARY - DAY   7

An agitated Giles stands with Xander, both examining the BOOK
CAGE.

                              GILES
                    We'll have to re-check every possible
                    exit avenue.

                              XANDER
                    I'm telling you, it's a waste of
                    time. I was here all night-

Now a post smooch Willow and Oz enter, looking mussed and
happy. Giles stiffens a little when he sees them.

                              GILES
                    Right then. Good to see you. No
                    need to panic.

Oz and Willow look at each other. Uh oh.

                              OZ
                              (to Giles)
                    Just a thought? Poker. Not your
                    game.

                              WILLOW
                    What's the deal, Giles?

                              GILES
                    Now. Keep in mind - most likely -
                    there is no deal.
                              (more)

                                                          CONTINUED

7   CONTINUED: 7

> GILES (cont'd)
> But if there was a deal it would
> concern a murder last night. A male
> student was found in the woods-

> WILLOW
> Which student?

> GILES
> Jeff Walken.

> OZ
> Jeff? He was - I know him.

> GILES
> I'm afraid... He was terribly
> mauled. And while I hate to think
> it, it could be the handiwork of-

> OZ
> (darkly)
> Me.

Willow takes his hand, anxious.

> WILLOW
> Wolf you. Not _you_ you.

Now Xander, examining the cage, puts in his two cents.

> XANDER
> But it's not. Not wolf you - or you
> you. Okay? The room was secure.
> The cage was locked. The window's
> unbreakable and-

As he speaks he taps a HIGH WINDOW which is laced with
security wire. It SWINGS OPEN.

> XANDER (cont'd)
> -open.

> WILLOW
> Oh, God.

> XANDER
> Hey. Not to freak. I rested my eyes now and
> then. That's all.

Giles speaks carefully - trying to contain his rising anger.

CONTINUED

7   CONTINUED: (2)   7

                         GILES
              And how long - exactly - did you
              "rest your eyes" for?

                         XANDER
              A little now. A little then. But I
              never heard Oz leave and he was here
              in the morning when I... when I-

                         GILES
              Woke up?

                         XANDER
              If you want to put it that way, Mr.
              Technical.

     Willow holds Oz' hand even harder.

                         WILLOW
              Oh, God.

     OFF OZ AND WILLOW

     Their faces etched with worry.

8   INT. COUNSELOR'S OFFICE - DAY   8

     Buffy arrives for her counseling session. The office sports
     standard school shrink decor - "Your Brain On Drugs" posters,
     etc. But there are also a few surprising touches of whimsy.

     The shrink, MR. PLATT, faces away from Buffy in a high back chair.
     All we see of him is one hand, which holds a smoking cigarette.

                         MR. PLATT
              The two o'clock. Buffy Summers.

                         BUFFY
              Buffy Summers, reporting for
              sanity... look, I know I have to do
              this and I'll cooperate, look at ink
              blots, but I don't want to talk about
              my childghood or my life or...
              anything, actually, and I don't want
              to be friends --

                         MR. PLATT
              We're not going to be friends.

     This stops her. The chair turns slowly around to reveal a
     surprisingly warm and okay guy.

                                                      CONTINUED

As he talks, he takes a last drag, stubs out the cig, hides
the ashtray in a drawer from which he pulls a can of air
freshener and sprays, puts it back and shuts the drawer.

              MR. PLATT (cont'd)
     You already have friends -- I hope.
     A friend is a good thing. Likes you,
     agrees with you, tells you what you
     want to hear. You don't need that
     right now. What you do need is a
     trained, not-too-crazy professional
     who will always give you his honest
     opinion. Which I offer you.
               (then)
     Have a seat.

Buffy does.

              BUFFY
     Not too crazy. Those are your
     credentials?

              MR. PLATT
               (points to
                certificates on the
                wall)
     Those are my credentials. Look,
     Buffy. Any person - grown up,
     shrink, pope, any person who claims
     to be totally sane is either lying or
     not very bright. Everybody has
     problems. Everyone has demons.
     Right?

Buffy can't help herself. She's starting to like this guy.

              BUFFY
     Gotta say I'm with you on that one.

              MR. PLATT
     Excellent. So, the hope I bring you
     is that demons can be fought. People
     can change. You can change. It's
     all about finding your strength.
     Believing in yourself.
               (then)
     Now. Your turn. Let's start with
     why you ran away.

              BUFFY
     It's a long story.

                                             CONTINUED

8 CONTINUED: (2)   8

                    MR. PLATT
          Bore me.

                    BUFFY
          I'm telling you - I'm so over it. I
          feel good. I'm moving on. I'm even
          dating someone new.

                    MR. PLATT
          All nice things. But still - you're
          bringing me in at the end of the
          movie.

Buffy sighs. She's not getting out of this.

                    BUFFY
          I was seeing this guy. It ended
          badly. And my mom and I were
          fighting... I kind of flipped.

                    MR. PLATT
          Tell me more about this guy. The bad-
          ending guy.

                    BUFFY
          He was the first person- I loved
          him. But then...

                    MR. PLATT
          He changed.

                    BUFFY
          Yes.

                    MR. PLATT
          He got mean.

                    BUFFY
          Yes.

                    MR. PLATT
          But you didn't stop loving him.
                    (off her silence)
          You know - lots of people lose
          themselves in love. It's no shame.
          They write songs about it.
                    (then)
          The hitch is - you can't stay lost.
          Sooner or later, you have to get
          back to yourself.

                    BUFFY
          And if you can't?

                                              CONTINUED

8   CONTINUED: (3)   8

                        MR. PLATT
          If you can't - love becomes your
          master. And you're just its dog.

9   INT. LIBRARY - DAY   9

     Buffy enters - thoughtful after seeing Platt. She stops when
     she sees the grave expressions of Giles, Xander, Cordy,
     Willow and Oz.

                        BUFFY
          I'm afraid to ask.

                        CORDELIA
          Oz ate someone last night.

                        WILLOW
          He did not!

                        XANDER
                   (to Cordy/stern)
          Oz does not eat people. It's more,
          werewolf play. You know - I bat you
          around a little bit. Like a cat toy.
          I have harmless wolf fun. Is it Oz'
          fault that, you know, side effect,
          people get cut to ribbons and maybe
          then he takes a little nibble and I'm
          not helping am I?

                        GILES
                   (to Buffy)
          Oz may have gotten out of his cage
          last night and-

     Oz cuts him off - his tone grim.

                        OZ
          Or there just happened to be another
          werewolf roaming the woods.

                        GILES
          Perhaps. Or perhaps it was something
          else entirely. Let's not overreact-

                        OZ
                   (frustrated)
          Good in theory. Not very helpful for
          the potential nibbler.

                                              CONTINUED

9 CONTINUED: 9

                         GILES
          That's why we all have to work to
          find out what happened.

                         BUFFY
          I'll patrol the woods.
                    (to Willow and the
                     others)
          You guys try to get into the morgue.

                         WILLOW
          Right, we can see if it's a werewolf
          kill or not. But what about Oz?

                         GILES
          Why don't we have Faith come watch
          over him.

                         OZ
          You're having a slayer watch me?
          Good thing we're not over-reacting.

Freaking - Oz heads for the library doors. But he stops. A
beat. He turns back.

                         OZ (cont'd)
          Okay. You know that thing where you
          bail in the middle of an upsetting
          conversation? I need to do that.
          Kind of dramatic. But sometimes it's
          a necessary guy thing.

He starts out again - but Willow moves to stop him.

                         WILLOW
          And I want you to. Do the guy
          thing - but...

She looks at the clock. It's half past five. Oz follows her
gaze - gets it. Has to fight all his instinct to bolt.
Supremely frustrated - he walks to the cage, closes the door.

ON WILLOW, OZ, AND THE CAGE

Willow moves to him - feeling for him.

                         WILLOW (cont'd)
              Oz...

He can't even look at her.

                         OZ
          Get away from the cage.

                                            CONTINUED

                         192

9 CONTINUED: (2)   9

                         WILLOW
          What?

                         OZ
          It's going to happen soon. Get away
          from me.

Willow, devastated, backs off.

                                        FADE TO:

10 EXT. WOODS - NIGHT   10

The night time woods are extra spooky. Buffy walks alone, a
little wigged.

CRACK!

Buffy jumps at the sound of a twig breaking. She peers into
the tangled vines and tree branches surrounding her.
Nothing.

She takes a deep breath - pushes on.

SOMETHING CRASHES THROUGH THE BUSHES NEAR HER

This time it's not a question - Buffy SPRINTS in the
direction of the noise. Stops, trying to get her bearings.

Again she's greeted by silence. The creature is lying low.

WHOOSH! Silhouetted against the FULL MOON, the MAN/BEAST
CREATURE races by Buffy and KNOCKS her to the ground. She
leaps back up - stake raised - ready for battle.

And she stops - frozen - at what she sees.

ANGEL

Feral. Mouth stained with dried blood. Eyes full of animal
rage.

                                        BLACK OUT.

                    END OF ACT ONE

ACT TWO

11   EXT. WOODS - NIGHT   11

Back to Angel and Buffy. She's so taken aback at seeing
him - so completely stunned - that she barely reacts as HE
BARRELS INTO HER AGAIN, knocking her down. Hard.

ON BUFFY

Fighting to get back on her feet. The sound of ANGEL'S
SNARLING APPROACH through the bushes seems to surround her.
He comes at her again. But this time she's ready - meets his
oncoming velocity with a HEAD BUTT.

Now they TANGLE on the ground. Buffy gets in a few good
licks but ANGEL is still BRUTALLY strong - she's having
trouble making any real gains.

Finally, Buffy manages to get to her feet. She races
ahead - disappearing into the dark shadows of the forest.

ON ANGEL

Who stops dead. His instincts working overtime. It's clear
to us that this is not the Angel we knew. He's more beast
than man.

WHOOSH!

Buffy SWINGS FROM A TREE BRANCH and DRIVES RIGHT INTO HIM -
knocking the WIND OUT OF HIM as he SLAMS TO THE GROUND. Now
she straddles him and CLOCKS him with a BRUTAL UPPERCUT.
He's out.

Buffy looks around. Sees a number of small eviscerated
ANIMAL CARCASSES littering the ground near by.

CLOSE ON BUFFY

Breathing hard. On total overload.

12   INT. MORGUE - NIGHT   12

Willow makes her way with a flashlight through the dark
morgue. Checks the names on a few body drawers until she
finds what she was looking for.

She opens the drawer - silently reacts to the horribly
thrashed body we can (thankfully) barely see. Swallows hard.

CONTINUED

12   CONTINUED: 12

Then she opens a plastic LUNCH BOX (Scooby Doo?) which
contains her "autopsy" tools; a scalpel, a pair of tweezers,
some cotton swabs, a couple of plastic baggies, etc...   She's
so preoccupied that she doesn't notice the SHADOWY FIGURE
MOVE behind her.

                    XANDER (O.C.)
                    (aghast)
               God...

IT'S JUST XANDER - who looks quickly away from the body.   To
gaze on this dude is clearly more than a mere mortal can
handle.   But Willow keeps her cool.

                    WILLOW
                    (hands him a baggie)
               Here.   Hold this open.

He takes it - still looking away.   Willow scrapes some stuff
from under the corpse's fingernails with a swab and deposits
the swab into the bag.

Now, unnoticed, CORDELIA steps from the darkness.   Touches
Xander's arm.   Xander startled, freaks.

                    XANDER
               We're doing crime, Cordy.   You don't
               sneak up during crime!

                    CORDELIA
               God.   Have a-

But she stops when she sees the body - she TRIPS.   Covers her
eyes.

                    CORDELIA (cont'd)
               Okay.   Scarred for life.

                    XANDER
               I think both "scarred" and "life" are
               moot for this fella, Cordy.

                    CORDELIA
               Not him - me.   Willow, how can you
               stand it?

                    XANDER
               Yeah, Will.   This guy is barf-worthy.
               Can't we be elsewhere?   Is Oz cleared
               or what?

                                                    CONTINUED

195

12 CONTINUED: (2)   12

                            WILLOW
                I'm not sure. I mean, there are a
                lot of incised wounds - but they
                could be from anything.

                            CORDELIA
                Anything with really big, sharp teeth
                and-

Xander turns his flashlight on her, cutting her off.

                            XANDER
                Do you want to go back to the car
                and wait?

                            CORDELIA
                What? I'm just saying-

                            WILLOW
                Almost done. Let me just get a few
                stray hairs off the body. They may
                be from the attacker...

Willow uses her tweezers and carefully removes some hairs.

                            XANDER
                Great. So we got everything we need?

                            WILLOW
                        (to Xander)
                Yeah. That's it.

And WILLOW FAINTS, falling right out of frame. Xander and
Cordelia react, moving to help her.

                            XANDER
                        (worried)
                Okay - little too much excitement for
                the Willster...
                        (to Cordy)
                It doesn't look too good for Oz, does it?

                            CORDELIA
                        (no duh)
                It really doesn't. This guy was
                ripped apart by a wild animal.

13 INT. MANSION - NIGHT   13

    CLOSE ON

    AN OLD TRUNK

                                                            CONTINUED

13 CONTINUED: 13

     Which BUFFY, working in a panicked rush, dumps over. We see
     a bunch of DRUSILLA'S DOLLS and other personal items spill
     onto the floor. At the bottom of the trunk are some long
     lengths of CHAIN and some WRIST SHACKLES.

     ANOTHER ANGLE

     Breathing hard - both from effort and fear - BUFFY threads a
     length of CHAIN through one of the ORNAMENTAL WALL MOUNTS
     bolted to the wall in the main room of the mansion.

     ANOTHER ANGLE

     Buffy SLAPS a SHACKLE around a wrist...

     AND NOW WE SEE ANGEL

     Who struggles against Buffy as she binds his other wrist. We
     see now that the chains are long enough that Angel can sit
     and move - a little.

     Finished, Buffy sits back heavily - exhausted.

     She stares at Angel - in a state of shock. Angel, tugging at
     his restraints, gives no sign that he's still aware of her in
     the room. Much less aware of who she is to him.

     Buffy starts to get up -- notices the BLACK SCORCH MARKS on
     the floor where Angel returned. She moves to them - runs a
     finger through the dark soot, puzzled...

14 INT. LIBRARY - NIGHT   14

     FAITH, listening to music on a walkman, DANCES in front of
     Oz's cage. She's really jamming and doesn't see BUFFY ENTER.

     Buffy glances at OZ, who is locked up - in wolf mode. Post
     Angel, Buffy finds the sight of him heavily unsettling.

     Now Buffy moves to Faith - who is bopping away from her.
     Buffy gently taps her shoulder. Faith spins and SMASHES
     BUFFY in the face. Hard. Buffy stumbles back.

                         BUFFY
                Oww - !

     Faith sees what she's done. Rips the headphones off. We can
     HEAR strains of SCREAMING HEAVY METAL through them.

                         FAITH
                Buffy! Are you okay!? What are you
                doing here?

                                                        CONTINUED

14   CONTINUED: 14

                              BUFFY
                    Bleeding internally. But I'll live.

                              FAITH
                    God, I'm sorry... I didn't hear you.

                              BUFFY
                    I figured. Ow - again.
                         (then)
                    I came to give you the rest of the
                    night off.

                              FAITH
                    Get out of jail free, huh? How come?

                              BUFFY
                    Can't sleep. Figured I'd cram for my
                    French test.

Faith grabs her stuff. Tosses Buffy the key to Oz' cage.

                              FAITH
                    Cool. I was going nuts in here. I
                    bet I can still get in a few good
                    stakings before sunrise.

                              BUFFY
                    Knock yourself out. But not
                    literally.

                              FAITH
                    Later.

And she's gone. Buffy watches after her for a beat - then
turns and goes to the library card file. She pulls a file
drawer out and carries it back to the table. . .

                                        FADE TO:

15   INT. LIBRARY - DAY   15

Early the next morning, Giles enters the library and moves
to the cage - sees Oz, back to his human self, safe and sound
and curled in a little nekkid ball. Giles unlocks the cage.

Now he turns and is surprised to find BUFFY asleep at the
table. She's surrounded by books on stuff like REINCARNATION
and ALTERNATE DIMENSIONS... Giles picks up one of the
books - examines it more closely. Sensing him, Buffy wakes.

                              BUFFY
                    Hey...

                                        CONTINUED

15   CONTINUED: 15

Now she realizes that it's GILES. She stands abruptly -
starts to close the books.

                    BUFFY (cont'd)
               Hey! Can you believe Faith and these
               nutty books?

He's not buying it. Reads a few book titles aloud.

                    GILES
               "Exploring Demon Dimensions." "The
               Mystery of Acathla..."

                    BUFFY
               I know! And she still listens to
               <u>heavy</u> <u>metal</u>. Freaky deaky.

                    GILES
               Buffy.

Buffy drops the act. Sits. She knows she's busted.

                    BUFFY
               What if I told you... I had a dream
               about Angel. And it brought up some
               questions.

                    GILES
               I'd say it was to be expected.
                    (re: card file)
               But it must have been quite a dream.
               I didn't think you knew what these
               cards were for.

                    BUFFY
               Yeah. I dreamt that he came back.

Now Giles sits.

                    GILES
               Of course. After Jenny was killed -
               I had dreams that she was still
               alive. That I saved her.

                    BUFFY
               But this dream was vivid. Really
               vivid. I mean, three-dimensional,
               sensurround, the hills are alive-

Giles' face registers concern.

                    BUFFY (cont'd)
               You get my point.

                                             CONTINUED

15 CONTINUED: (2)   15

                         GILES
               Do you believe it was a prophecy?

                         BUFFY
                    (carefully)
               No. I don't know. It just made me
               wonder. I mean - is there a chance,
               even? Could it happen?

          Giles considers. Just the prospect makes him uncomfortable.

                         GILES
               There's no record of someone
               returning from a demon dimension once   *
               the "gate" has closed. I can't   *
               imagine how it would happen or why.

                         BUFFY
               Okay. But let's pretend - wacky
               world - he somehow ended up here in
               Sunnydale again. I mean, what would
               he be like?

                         GILES
               I can't really say. What little is
               known about the dimension accessed
               via Acathla suggests a world of
               brutal torment. And time in demon
               worlds moves quite different than
               here-

                         BUFFY
               Yeah. I remember... So - Angel
               would have been there for, like,
               close to a hundred years?

                         GILES
               Yes.

                         BUFFY
               Of torture.

                         GILES
                    (nods)
               Only a person with tremendous will
               and character could survive that and
               retain any semblance of self.

          Buffy reels from this news.

                         BUFFY
               He'd be a monster. A lost cause.

                                                         CONTINUED

15   CONTINUED: (3)   15

                         GILES
          Maybe... Maybe not. In my
          experience, there are two kinds of
          monsters. The first type can be
          redeemed. And, more importantly,
          they want to be redeemed...

                         BUFFY
          And the second type?

                         GILES
          The second - is void of humanity. It
          can not respond to reason. Or love.

Buffy takes this in, freaked, when-

WILLOW

Enters with a bakery bag in hand. Sees Buffy, who is still
tripping from the conversation with Giles.

                         WILLOW
          I thought Faith was on duty.

                         BUFFY
          Change of plans.

Willow opens the bag - holds it out. It's full of donuts.

                         WILLOW
          Glazed or cake? It's fun to watch
          them make them, you know. They have
          this spritzy thing that plops the
          batter right-

                         BUFFY
                    (interrupting)
          You couldn't sleep either?

                         WILLOW
          I've been sitting in Mr. Donut since
          the TV did that snowy thing.
                    (then)
          But, how come you're wakey-girl? I
          mean, this time it's not your
          boyfriend who may be a cold blooded-

Willow's startled by OZ, WHO STEPS FROM THE CAGE, buttoning
his shirt.

                         WILLOW (cont'd)
          -jelly donut.

                                                    CONTINUED

15 CONTINUED: (4)   15

    She holds the bag out to Oz. Smiles too big.

                        OZ
              Everything okay?

                        BUFFY
              Yeah - what happened with the
              inspection of the body?

                        WILLOW
                   (re: donuts)
              Anybody? They're yummy delicious.

                        BUFFY
                   (anxious)
              Come on, Will. Was it a werewolf...
                   (quietly)
              Was it a vampire?

    They just look at her. She bites the bullet.

                        WILLOW
              It wasn't conclusive. I-

    Buffy interrupts, intense.

                        BUFFY
              How could you not conclude? I mean,
              what did it look like? Was he bit?

                        GILES
                   (cutting her off)
              Let her finish, Buffy.

                        BUFFY
              It's just... Sorry.

    Willow glances at Oz - worried.

                        WILLOW
              I should know more after tonight.
              I'm doing hair and fiber tests.

                        OZ
              You know how to do those?

                        WILLOW
                   (caught)
              Not- I... like to sound technical
              when I'm scared. But I figure - wolf
              hair, hair found on the body. See if
              they match. It's a test.

                                                    CONTINUED

15   CONTINUED: (5)   15

                         OZ
            So we're scared now. It's official.

                         WILLOW
            What? Oh - no - I didn't mean it
            that way-

                         OZ
            No. I'd say scared is pretty much
            called for. It's cool.

    ON BUFFY

    Thinking about Angel. Knowing as well as the others that
    it's not cool. Not at all.

16   INT. CAFETERIA - DAY   16

    Buffy moves through the crowded room with her lunch tray,
    trying to find a table. Sees SCOTT sitting with Debbie and
    Pete. He waves her over. A beat - then Buffy pastes on a
    smile and joins them.

                         SCOTT
            Can't back you on this lunch.
            Nutritional demerits.

    Buffy glances at her tray. She has three different kinds of
    Jello - and nothing else.

                         BUFFY
            My stomach doesn't want hard food.
            There's fruit stuff in there.

                         SCOTT
            Those are marshmallows.

                         BUFFY
            Oh...
                 (then)
            I'm kinda out of it today. Didn't
            sleep well.

                         DEBBIE
            Just don't tell Mr. Platt you've got
            insomnia. He'll make you start a
            "dream journal."

                                                    CONTINUED

16 CONTINUED: 16

                              PETE
               What's that - like a Barbie thing?
               "Dear Dream Journal, why hasn't Ken
               come around since he got that
               earring..?"

                              DEBBIE
               I never did it. He's a quack.

                              BUFFY
               I sort of thought he was cool.

                              DEBBIE
               Really?
                    (trying)
               I guess he can be funny and stuff.
               It's just - I don't like the things
               he says sometimes.

                              BUFFY
               Yeah. He definitely marches to the
               beat of his own drummer. In fact -
               I think he makes his own drums.

                              SCOTT
               My mom says therapy can be completely
               helpful-

                              PETE
               Your Mom has the wattage of a Zippo
               lighter, Scott.

Debbie tries to stifle a laugh. Scott takes Pete's barbs in
stride. He puts a protective hand on Buffy's leg.

                              SCOTT
               I hope you realize I don't actually
               know these people. I just thought
               you'd like me better if I had
               friends - so I hired them.

Now he moves closer - shutting out Pete and Debbie and
getting kind of boyfriend-y. Buffy smiles - but it's clear
she's uncomfortable.

                              SCOTT (cont'd)
                    (then/quietly)
               So - I wanted to tell you that you
               look great today. But now I want to
               raise that to amazing because you
               didn't sleep well.

                                                        CONTINUED

16   CONTINUED: (2)   16

He's making smitten eyes at her. Buffy knows she should be
making them back - but she's too spun.

                    BUFFY
          God. That's incredibly-

She pulls away from him. Starts to get up from the table.

                    BUFFY (cont'd)
          -sweet... And I wish I didn't have
          to... But I just remembered... that
          I do... I'll see you.

She smiles sort of wanly at the table and takes off - leaving
them all at a loss.

                    PETE
          Check out Scott. Liking the manic-
          depressive chick.

Scott shoots Pete a seriously warning look. Pete backs off.

                    PETE (cont'd)
          Kidding, my friend. She's special.
          Like two very hot girlfriends in one.

ON BUFFY

Rushing out of the cafeteria. Losing it.

17   INT. MANSION - DAY   17

Buffy enters. Finds Angel shaking as if he is freezing and
huddled in a corner - his restraints still firmly in place.
He turns his gaze on her, watches her intently, silently...
She moves a little closer - instinctively, he moves back.

                    BUFFY
          Angel? Can you - ?

He just looks at her. She tries again - reaches tentatively
out and TOUCHES HIM.

And Angel SNARLS like a wounded dog - as if he's been touched
by acid. Shackled hands fly out to defend himself. And his
eyes burn into Buffy. Angry - unrecognizing.

BUFFY

Falls away from him. Startled, mortified, she takes off.

CLOSE ON ORNAMENTAL WALL MOUNT

                                                    CONTINUED

17   CONTINUED: 17

    As it LOOSENS a bit from the pressure on Angel's restraints.

18   EXT. SCHOOL GROUNDS - DAY   18

    The fall light melts into late afternoon amber as we see
    PETE, coaxing a nervous, giggling Debbie toward the GARDEN
    SHED that sits back on the school property.

                    PETE
       Come on - just for a minute...

                    DEBBIE
       I can't. I have to meet a friend-

19   INT. SCHOOL - GARDEN SHED - DAY   19

    Now Pete pulls her inside the shed. The place is obviously
    frequented by lusty teenagers. The walls are COVERED WITH
    HEARTS AND INITIALS. Pete pulls Debbie into his arms. She
    submits in short order and they kiss hungrily. He tries to
    move her into a darker part of the shed, but Debbie pulls
    away - nervous.

                    DEBBIE
       No. Let - Let's stay here.

                    PETE
       What's with you today? Relax...

    Pete grabs her. They start to go at it again. Then Pete
    opens his eyes in the midst of a smooch - notices a BOTTLE on
    one of the SHELVES BEHIND DEBBIE. It's EMPTY - but the
    remnants of a GLOWING, EERIE GREEN liquid cling to the inside
    of the bottle. He pulls back from her.

                   PETE (cont'd)
       What is that?

                    DEBBIE
       Nothing. Kiss me.

    Debbie tries to pull him back into an embrace - clearly not
    wanting him to see the bottle. But it's too late. He looks
    at Debbie, shocked.

                    PETE
       You didn't drink that, did you?

                    DEBBIE
       Drink it? You - you know I didn't.

                                      CONTINUED

19   CONTINUED: 19

But Pete doesn't buy it. He's freaking.

                         PETE
              Debbie... What's going on?

20   INT. SCHOOL - HALLWAY - DAY   20

Buffy moves purposefully down the hallway

21   INT. COUNSELOR'S OFFICE - DAY   21

The door is open a crack. Buffy looks in. Sees that Mr.
Platt is there. He's smoking, turned away from her in his
chair - the way he was the first time she came to see him.
Buffy starts to pace - anxious.

                         BUFFY
              Two o'clock, Buffy right. Don't turn
              around and don't say anything. Just
              listen. That's your thing, right?
                   (with difficulty)
              Something's going on... I mean, the
              whole entire story will probably
              convince you I'm like, loony bin
              material. But I can't tell
              anybody - not Willow, not Giles,
              nobody... They'd just freak out on
              me or maybe do something... And
              I'm... I need help.
                   (near tears)
              I need to talk to someone. I'm so
              scared. I -- this guy, he...

Buffy stops her confession when she sees that the CIGARETTE
in Platt's hand is ALL ASH - burned down to his fingers.

                         BUFFY (cont'd)
              ... he's come back...

Now we come around the chair to see that Platt has been
HORRIBLY MURDERED. Ripped to shreds. The work of a terrible
beast.
                                        BLACK OUT.

                         END OF ACT TWO

ACT THREE

22   INT. SCHOOL - GARDEN SHED - DAY   22

Back to Debbie, Pete and that GLOWING BOTTLE OF LIQUID.
Debbie is clearly terrified as Pete, bottle in hand,
continues his interrogation of her. His tone is different
now - both menacing and condescending.

                    PETE
              So - the bottle jumped out of the
              cabinet and spilled on its own?

                    DEBBIE
              Of course not-

He advances on her. Debbie meekly retreats.

                    DEBBIE (cont'd)
              I - I was just trying to get rid of
              it.

Pete's anger shifts to icy rage at this confession.

                    PETE
              You were trying to get rid of it.

                    DEBBIE
              To help you. You know how you get-

Pete grabs Debbie - holds the bottle close to her face.
Debbie flinches, her terror growing.

ANGLE: PETE'S HAND

Clenched into a fist -- the veins in the back of it throbbing
menacingly.

                    PETE
              You think this has anything to do
              with "how I get?"

                    DEBBIE
              Well, when you drink it-

                    PETE
              When I drink it - nothing! I don't
              need it anymore, Debbie. I'm past
              that now-

He yanks Debbie ROUGHLY over to a line of shelves. Amid the
PESTICIDES and GARDEN FERTILIZERS, we see more ODD LIQUIDS
AND CHEMISTRY SET TYPE STUFF.

                                                    CONTINUED

22 CONTINUED: 22

He grabs the bottles and beakers and starts to SMASH THEM on
the ground - steadily losing control.

                    PETE (cont'd)
          See? No more! You can pour out
          everything I made and it won't
          help - and you want to know why?

Debbie just shakes her head. Pete grips her harder-

                    PETE (cont'd)
          You know why? Because all it takes
          is <u>you</u> now, Debbie. You and your
          stupid, grating voice-

Suddenly - Pete's HEAD STARTS TO THRASH WILDLY and he SCREAMS
WITH RAGE.

Just as abruptly, his head STOPS - and we see that a chilling
transformation has taken place. Pete has turned into a RAGE
MONSTER. An ADRENALINE PUMPED, VEINY creature with razor
sharp teeth and claws.

Debbie watches - frozen, petrified. She knows what's coming.
Now Pete BELLOWS at her - his voice a garbled bark.

                    PETE (cont'd)
          <u>You're</u> the reason I started with the
          formulas in the first place - to be
          the man <u>you</u> wanted. And you pay me
          back, how? You whore around with
          other guys and taunt-

                    DEBBIE
          No! I don't! I don't even look-

WHAM! Pete brutally SMACKS - sending her reeling.

                    PETE
          I was <u>talking</u>! Is that something
          your shrink taught you, Debbie - to
          "share?" To "communicate?" To piss
          me off?

He advances on her again. Picks her up from the floor.
She's crying now.

                    PETE (cont'd)
          Well, guess what? Even he's not
          going to listen to your pathetic
          ramblings anymore-

                                              CONTINUED

22   CONTINUED: (2)   22

      BAM! Another hit and Debbie collapses. Pete stands over
      her - shaking with rage.

                          PETE (cont'd)
                I'm all you've got, Debbie. You hear
                me?! I'm all you've got!

      Debbie nods through her tears, wipes a trickle of blood from
      her mouth. It seems her sobs have an impact on him. As it
      dawns on him what he's done - his expression softens. The
      adrenaline seems to DRAIN from his body.

                          PETE (cont'd)
                Ah, hell. God...

      And just as suddenly as he changed - PETE DEFLATES, changing
      back to his normal self. (**CGI**) Non-monster Pete is instantly
      repentant. He moves to Debbie, gathers her in his arms.

                          PETE (cont'd)
                Baby, you okay?

      Debbie, in shock, nods "yes". He kisses her forehead.

                          PETE (cont'd)
                You know you shouldn't make me mad.
                You know what happens.
                     (off her silence)
                Please, Debbie. You alright?

      A beat. Finally, Debbie wraps her arms around him and they
      rock together. When she speaks - her tone is soothing.

                          DEBBIE
                It's okay... It's okay...

23   INT. LIBRARY - DAY   23

      Willow and Faith sit with a shaken Buffy. Giles paces.

                          GILES
                This creature is especially brutal.
                I think the charming phrase the
                coroner used when describing Mr.
                Platt was "pureed." But he did
                confirm that Platt had been dead just
                a few hours when Buffy found him.

                          FAITH
                Which means that the guy was killed during
                the day.

                                                      CONTINUED

23   CONTINUED: 23

Buffy's reaction to this is tempered. She's seen Platt. But
Willow can't hide her joy. She punches a fist in the air.

                    WILLOW
          Yes!

Everyone looks at her. She slowly lowers her hand.

                    WILLOW (cont'd)
          Sorry. I got a little... I mean,
          it's horrible. Horrible.

                    BUFFY
          It's okay, Will. We're all glad Oz
          is off the hook.

                    GILES
               (concerned)
          Indeed. But shouldn't he be here by
          now? The sun sets at half past five.

24   EXT. FOUNTAIN COURT - DAY   24

Speaking of... OZ waits by the fountain, checks his watch.
He starts to bail - when he's stopped by a breathless DEBBIE.

                    DEBBIE
          Sorry I'm late. Did you bring the
          notes?

She's all smiles - trying to finish their business and move
on before he picks up on her black eye and streaked make-up.
But Oz, handing her the notes, catches on to the weirdness.

                    OZ
          You okay?

                    DEBBIE
          What? Oh, yeah. I'm such a klutz.
          I, uh...

Oz nods knowingly.

                    OZ
          Fell down and hit your... eye.

                    DEBBIE
          Door knob.
               (re: notes)
          Thanks.

She starts to take off - Oz puts a hand on her arm.

                                                    CONTINUED

24   CONTINUED: 24

                              OZ
                    Hey. If you want to talk-

Debbie sighs. She's heard this before.

OTHER END OF FOUNTAIN COURT

As PETE arrives, unnoticed by them. He sees Oz and Debbie
talking closely. It doesn't sit well with him.

ON DEBBIE AND OZ

Still unaware that Pete is watching. Debbie is momentarily
swayed Oz' concern - puts her own hand on his for a moment.

                              DEBBIE
                    I-
                         (thinks better of it)
                    Thanks again for the notes.

She pulls away - takes off. Oz debates going after her. But
it's too close to sunset. He moves toward the school.

25   INT. LIBRARY - DAY   25

Buffy, Giles, Faith and Willow continue the discussion of Mr.
Platt's killer.

                              GILES
                    Our task now is to determine what
                    sort of killer we're dealing with-

Now Oz enters. Unnoticed by the others, he overhears Giles'
next comment.

                              GILES (cont'd)
                    Clearly we're looking for a depraved,
                    sadistic animal.

Oz steps forward. Grim.

                              OZ
                    Present.
                         (glances at Willow)
                    Hey. I may be a cold blooded jelly
                    donut - but my timing's impeccable.

Willow can't contain herself. Runs to him, excited.

                                                        CONTINUED

25   CONTINUED: 25

                         WILLOW
               But you're not! It's a "kill in the
               day" monster! One-hundred percent
               for sure.

A beat as Oz takes this in. Nodding.

                         OZ
               Okay.

Filled with relief - they hug. Giles gives them a moment
before getting back on task.

                         GILES
               I wish we had time to celebrate
               properly. Unfortuntely, it's
               imperative that we find out who or
               what is doing this.
                         (then)
               Now. We have two victims. Jeff
               Walken, and now Platt. Perhaps they
               have something in common-   *

                         FAITH
               Missing internal organs?

                         GILES
               Besides that.

Oz's wheels are turning.

                         OZ
               Debbie.

All eyes turn to him.

                         OZ (cont'd)
               Victim #1. Jeff? He was in Jazz
               band with us. They used to horse
               around.

                         FAITH
               They were screwing?

                         OZ
               I don't think so. But he hid her
               music comp book once.

                         BUFFY
               Good enough. And we know Debbie knew
               Mr. Platt. She was seeing him and
               way vocal about not having the love
               for the guy.

                                                          CONTINUED

25 CONTINUED: (2)   25

                         OZ
             Add this and stir. I ran into her
             just now - sporting a nasty black
             eye.

                         WILLOW
             Okay. Pretend Debbie wanted Platt
             dead. Maybe he fought back.

                         BUFFY
             No, he was dead in an instant.
             Didn't even lose his cigarette.

That's it. Buffy stands.

                         BUFFY (cont'd)
             Could be - boyfriend Pete's the one
             doling out the punishment.

Now everybody mobilizes.

                         GILES
             We have to find them both immediately.

                         OZ
             Deb was in the hall a minute ago.

                         GILES
             We should split up. Faith - you and
             I will team. Willow - you stick with
             Buffy.

Oz, stands - chimes in with the same urgency as the others.

                         OZ
             I'll - lock myself in the cage.

26 INT. GIRL'S LOCKER ROOM - DAY   26

We find Debbie at the mirror with her make-up bag. She's
trying to mask the bright purple bruises around her eye.

Now we see Buffy and Willow, who have just entered. They
observe Debbie for a moment. Then-

                         BUFFY
             It's tricky covering a fresh shiner
             like that. You know what works?

Debbie, startled, looks up from the mirror. Answers warily.

                                                    CONTINUED

26 CONTINUED: 26

                              DEBBIE
                    What?

                              BUFFY
                    Don't get hit.

Debbie's heard enough. Starts to gather her things. But
Buffy moves closer - her tone kind but determined.

                              BUFFY (cont'd)
                    What's going on, Debbie? I'd bet the
                    farm you know.

                              DEBBIE
                    You're wrong. I don't know anything.

                              BUFFY
                    Now - normally? I'd say - you want
                    to play "I have a secret" - fine.
                    But people are dying.

A long beat. Debbie, trapped, stammers-

                              DEBBIE
                    It's - it's not his fault. I mean,
                    he's not himself when he gets like
                    this...

Buffy and Willow exchange looks.

                              BUFFY
                    You mean Pete.

                              DEBBIE
                         (nods)
                    It's me. I make him crazy. He just
                    does what he does because he loves me
                    too much-

                              WILLOW
                    So it is him? But weren't Mr. Platt
                    and Jeff murdered by an animal?

Buffy gets it - fixes Debbie with a hard look.

                              BUFFY
                    Pete's... not like other guys, is he
                    Debbie?

It dawns on Debbie what she just did - that she gave Pete up.
She panics, starts for the door.

                                                        CONTINUED

26   CONTINUED: (2)   26

                         DEBBIE
                I - I've got to go.

Buffy blocks her.

                         BUFFY
                You have to talk to us. We can't
                help you until you do.

                         DEBBIE
                I didn't ask for your help.

                         WILLOW
                Well, when are you going to? I
                mean - if Pete kills you - it'll be
                pretty much too late.

                         BUFFY
                Debbie. We're running out of time.

OFF DEBBIE

Frightened despite herself.

27   INT. MANSION - DAY   27

We move across the cavernous room until we find Angel - who
pulls with all his might at the restraints. That wall mount
that was loosening? It finally gives and falls from the
wall. Although still in chains and shackles, he's not
secured to anything. He's free.

A moment, then he bolts out of frame.

28   INT. GIRL'S LOCKER ROOM - DAY   28

Back to Debbie, Buffy and Willow.

                         BUFFY
                Where can we find him, Debbie?

                         DEBBIE
                       (freaking)
                I - I don't know.

                         BUFFY
                You're lying.

Now Debbie tries to mask her fear with bravado.

                                                        CONTINUED

> DEBBIE
> What if I am. What are you going to
> do about it?

> WILLOW
> (wincing)
> Wrong question.

Frustrated now, Buffy takes Debbie and turns her toward the
mirror. Makes Debbie look at her bruised and swollen face.

> BUFFY
> Look at yourself. Why are you
> protecting him?

Debbie looks away. Doesn't answer.

> BUFFY (cont'd)
> Anybody who really loved you couldn't
> do this to you.

> DEBBIE
> He's going to change. He promised-

> BUFFY
> Maybe. At best 50/50. Lame odds
> when you're betting your life.

Debbie looks at them - confused, wavering.

> DEBBIE
> (meekly)
> Would they take him someplace?

> BUFFY
> Probably.

> DEBBIE
> (rising panic)
> Be away from Pete? I can't-

> WILLOW
> Of course you can. And we'll both
> help you. Believe me - we understand.
> (then)
> But you have to choose. It's got to
> be you over him.

The part where Debbie was wavering? It's over. Her eyes go
cold. She's shutting down.

CONTINUED

28 CONTINUED: (2)   28

> DEBBIE
> I could never do that to him. I'm
> his everything.

> BUFFY
> (losing patience)
> Great. While you guys enjoy your
> grim fairy-tale, two people are dead.
> Who's gonna be next?

29 INT. LIBRARY - DAY   29

Oz hangs out in the book cage - waiting for night to fall.
He looks up when the doors to the library swing open.

PETE

Still in human-mode, enters. Glowers at Oz.

> PETE
> Since when do you touch my girl?

Oz takes a beat. Assessing the situation. Then-

> OZ
> This is a really bad time, Pete.

> PETE
> Guess you weren't thinking about that
> when you put the moves on Debbie...

> OZ
> I talked to her, yeah. But it was
> move-free.

Pete advances, seething. Oz, a tad nervous now, glances at
the clock - tries to focus.

> OZ (cont'd)
> About this cage? When the sun sets-

> PETE
> You won't be alive to see it.

PETE starts to YANK ON THE CAGE DOOR, his face going red with
the effort.

> OZ
> I'm serious. Something happens,
> which you probably won't believe-

CONTINUED

29 CONTINUED: 29

> And with a mighty YELL Pete's HEAD STARTS TO THRASH AGAIN
> (**CGI**). He CHANGES INTO RAGE MONSTER PETE before Oz' eyes.

                    OZ (cont'd)
          -or you might.

> Now - after another RAGE FILLED BELOW, PETE finally RIPS THE
> DOOR FROM THE CAGE. Oz backs up, very calm with terror.

                              BLACK OUT.

                    END OF ACT THREE

ACT FOUR

30   INT. GIRL'S LOCKER ROOM - DAY   30

Buffy and Willow try to deal with Debbie - who has gone into
her own freaky world. She looks at herself in the mirror,
hugging herself and rocking, talking to no one in particular.

                    DEBBIE
          He does love me. He does love me...

                    BUFFY
          We'd better go - we have to find Pete.

Buffy takes Debbie gently by the arm - starts to lead her to
the door. Debbie continues to mutter-

                    DEBBIE
          He does love me. He does love me...

                    WILLOW
                (to Buffy/worried)
          I think we broke her.

                    BUFFY
                (sadly)
          I think she was broken before this.

31   INT. LIBRARY - CONT. - NIGHT   31

WHAMP! Oz hits the floor hard in the wake of a terrible blow
from monster Pete. Oz tries to stand but monster Pete KICKS
HIM, sending him sprawling once again...

Oz, crawling and wincing with pain, glances out the window,
sees the (STOCK SHOT) SUN SLIP FROM VIEW. We register just
a hint of relief across his features.

                    PETE
          Did you kiss that whore? Did she
          like it?

Now Pete LIFTS Oz back to his feet and is about to administer
another nasty thrashing - but Oz shoves him back with a firm
hand. Pete stumbles and hits the floor.

CLOSE ON CLOCK

Which reads just after 5:30.

RESUME

                                                        CONTINUED

31   CONTINUED: 31

                              OZ
                    Time's up. Rules change.

CLOSE ON OZ' EYE

As it goes WOLFY. (CGI)

RESUME

Baffled, monster Pete looks up in time to see OZ THE WEREWOLF
LUNGE for him - teeth bared.

Now the TWO MONSTERS go at it. It's a full-on, "When Animals
Attack" extravaganza.

Oz pounces Pete, and they roll on the floor in a growling,
snarling tangle.

Pete SLASHES OZ with a knife-like claw. Oz retaliates as he
LOCKS HIS POWERFUL JAW around Pete's forearm. Pete SCREAMS
in agony...

32   INT. SCHOOL - HALLWAY - CONT. - NIGHT   32

Buffy, Willow and Debbie move down the hall when they hear
PETE'S UNEARTHLY CRY coming from the library. FAITH and
GILES run in from outside, alarmed at the sound.

                              FAITH
                    What the hell - ?

33   INT. LIBRARY - CONT. - NIGHT   33

Buffy, Willow, Faith, Giles and Debbie enter to see werewolf
OZ and monster Pete engaged in serious battle.

OZ still has a HOWLING Pete by the arm, but now Pete uses the
position to FLIP OZ over on his back.

For a brief moment everyone stands and take the spectacle in,
agape. Then Buffy spies the TRANQUILIZER GUN on the table.
Grabs it. She aims at PETE... Her finger goes to the
trigger... She finds her shot...

DEBBIE
Pete! Watch out!

As Buffy shoots DEBBIE GRABS THE GUN, yanking IT TO ONE SIDE.
The shot goes wild AND <u>HITS GILES</u>.

CLOSE ON GILES

                                                    CONTINUED

                              221

33   CONTINUED: 33

                              GILES
                 Right.   Bloody priceless.

And he's OUT.

RESUME

Buffy shoves Debbie away -- and she slips out of sight,
forgotten by all. Giles falls INTO a book stand, which
TOPPLES right near OZ. Startled, OZ blows past them and OUT
THE LIBRARY DOORS.

Now BUFFY slams an off-guard Pete with a couple of serious
blows. Pete backs her off by TOPPLING A BOOKCASE in her
path - then disappears into the stacks.

Forgotten in all the confusion - Debbie also bails.

                              BUFFY
                 I'll take Pete.

Buffy tosses Faith the tranquilizer gun as she leaves. Faith
snatches it - heads for the hall with Willow on her heels.

                              FAITH
                 I got the wolf.

34   INT. SCHOOL - GARDEN SHED - NIGHT   34

Debbie enters the shed, calls uncertainly -

                              DEBBIE
                 Pete?

Nothing. Debbie moves into a dark corner - prepared to wait
for her man.

35   INT. SCHOOL - HALLWAY - NIGHT   35

MONSTER PETE runs through a hall with Buffy not far behind.
With a burst of determination, he sprints a good distance
ahead of her - rounds a corner and loses her for a moment-

36   INT. ANOTHER PART OF THE HALLWAY - NIGHT   36

Pete sees a HIGH OPEN WINDOW and LEAPS for it, barely holding
onto the sill with his bloodied, injured arm. He pulls
himself through just as BUFFY enters the hall. She stops -
surprised. He's nowhere to be seen.

                                                      CONTINUED

37   INT. SCHOOL - HALLWAY - NIGHT   37

Yet ANOTHER HALL - where Faith races after Oz, who is loping
along at an amazing pace.

Willow lags behind her, trying desperately to keep up.

38   INT. GARDEN SHED - NIGHT   38

Debbie JUMPS as the door to the shed slams. There,
silhouetted against the night is PETE, looming in all his
rage monster glory. Debbie rushes to him - throws herself
into his arms.

                    DEBBIE
          Pete - you're alright. God, you're
          alright...

She holds on tight - tries not to notice that he's not
returning her embrace.

                    DEBBIE (cont'd)
          She almost shot you - did you see?
          I stopped her.

Nothing. Debbie pulls back - babbles on.

                    DEBBIE (cont'd)
          You have to leave. Get out of
          Sunnydale. She knows-

Pete finally speaks - his voice eerily cool.

                    PETE
          How does she know, Debbie. Did you
          run your big mouth?

                    DEBBIE
          No! She just knew. I mean, it
          seemed like she knew-

He THROWS her out of his arms - she falls to the ground.

                    PETE
          So you filled in the blanks.

                    DEBBIE
          No-

He ADVANCES ON HER - his anger simmering and lethal.

                    PETE
          But what did I expect from a screw up
          like you?

                                        CONTINUED

38   CONTINUED: 38

                              DEBBIE
                    I - I didn't. Pete-

                              PETE
                    Fact is, Debbie? You're nothing but
                    a waste of space.

CLOSE ON DEBBIE

As a horrible certainty washes over her.

                              DEBBIE
                         No...

Now PETE'S BLACK SHADOW engulfs her.

39   INT. SCHOOL - ANOTHER PART OF THE HALLWAY - NIGHT   39

Buffy's back in the hall where she lost Pete. She stops -
notices his BLOOD HIGH on the wall by the window.

40   INT. SCHOOL - HALLWAY - NIGHT   40

Faith is gaining on Oz when he suddenly turns tail and RACES
TOWARD HER. Before she has time to react - HE PLOWS into her
and they both go tumbling to the ground. Faith drops the
tranquilizer gun and it goes skittering across the floor.

Willow, observing this from a distance, SCREAMS.

                              WILLOW
                    No! Down!! Bad Oz!

41   EXT. SCHOOL - NIGHT   41

Buffy jumps out of the window Pete escaped through. Sees
that she's standing right in front of the garden shed. And,
behind a grimy window, something seems to be moving inside.

42   INT. SCHOOL - GARDEN SHED - NIGHT   42

Buffy enters cautiously. DEBBIE'S body lies lifeless in the
corner.

                              BUFFY
                    Oh my god.

Buffy rushes to her - takes her pulse. Nothing.

                                                      CONTINUED

BUFFY THE VAMPIRE SLAYER "Beauty and the Beasts" (WHITE) 8/19/98   49.

42   CONTINUED: 42

Distracted by Debbie, Buffy doesn't see PETE move behind her.
He grabs her with vicious force - HURLS her into a wall.

43   INT. SCHOOL - HALLWAY - NIGHT   43

Where Faith and Oz battle on the floor. Faith, pinned
beneath him, manages to hold him off - but she won't be able
to for much longer. She yells to Willow-

                    FAITH
          The gun! Where's the gun!?

Willow searches the floor. Sees it under Oz' hind leg.
There's no way Faith can get to it. Willow makes a snap
decision. RUNS UP and PULLS OZ' TAIL. HARD.

                    WILLOW
          Get off her!

OZ SNARLS in protest - turns his steely EYES ON HER. Willow
starts to RUN.

                    WILLOW (cont'd)
          Get the gun, get the gun, get the
          gun!!

A beat, then a properly distracted OZ goes after Willow,
gaining on her easily. Faith scrambles for the gun.

                    WILLOW (cont'd)
          HURRY!

BOOM! Faith shoots Oz dead on. Willow hits the ground as Oz
TUMBLES PAST HER. Lands in a panting heap.

44   INT. SCHOOL - GARDEN SHED - NIGHT   44

This time Buffy's the victim of surprise. She falls HARD on
the ground. Doesn't have time to recover before Pete is on
her again, SLAMMING HER WITH BRUTAL PUNCH AFTER BRUTAL PUNCH.
She tries to fight, but Pete seems to GROW STRONGER AND
STRONGER with his growing FURY.

                    PETE
          All the same! You're all the same!

45   INT. SCHOOL - HALLWAY - NIGHT   45

Faith and Willow cautiously approach Oz - who is unable to
fend off the powerful drugs in his system.

                                                        CONTINUED

45 CONTINUED: 45

He lifts his head - looks at Willow - and with a grunt,
passes out. Willow reaches down and strokes his fur tenderly.

                    WILLOW
          We have to get you a better cage.

46 INT. SCHOOL - GARDEN SHED - NIGHT   46

Buffy, reeling from another hit, tries to get to her feet -
sees a shadow rise against the wall of the shed. She
turns - fists up, ready again to fight.

But IT'S ANGEL in the doorway -- in VAMPFACE. He still has
the LONG LENGTH OF CHAIN strung from one shackled wrtist to
the other. He powers toward her, yielding the chain like a
weapon. Buffy flinches - confused - is he coming for her?
But he flashes PAST HER AND LASHES PETE WITH THE CHAIN,
sending him reeling.

Recovering from the beating she took, Buffy watches, stunned,
as Pete slashes viciously at Angel with his claws. In
response, Angel wails on Pete with the chain - one mighty
blow after another - trying to knock the fight out of him.

Finally - Pete manages to get a hand on Angel's face -
cutting him and jabbing for his EYES. Angel falls back.

Now Pete LUNGES, razor claws bared, for an unprepared Buffy.

Angel sees this. With no time to think, he THROWS THE CHAIN
AROUND PETE'S NECK and YANKS IT TIGHT - snapping Pete's neck.

Angel extracts the chains and retreats. Pete falls, limp, to
the ground. A beat and his labored breathing stops. Then we
make along his lifeless body, revealing that he has CHANGED
INTO HIS NON-MONSTER SELF. Angel turns to Buffy.

CLOSE ON BUFFY AND ANGEL

As Angel approaches her. Buffy isn't sure what to do -
whether she should be on the defensive or not.

But before she can make up her mind, he MORPHS back to human
face and speaks his first human word - desperate and
hopeful...

                    ANGEL
          Buffy?

They lock eyes. It's him. She sees the kindness returned
there. The familiarity.

                                                    CONTINUED

46   CONTINUED: 46

She nods.

And with her affirmation - Angel falls to his knees at her
feet. Despite the chains and shackles, he wraps his arms
around her waist. Begins to cry as he feels the first
comfort he's known in a hundred years.

                    ANGEL (cont'd)
          Buffy...

ON BUFFY

Overwhelmed. Fighting her own tears. This can't be
happening.

                                        FADE TO:

47   EXT. FOUNTAIN COURTYARD - DAY   47

Xander, Cordy and Buffy are walking toward class. Oz and
Willow also walk with the group but are "paired," holding
hands and obviously recovering nicely from their wolfy trauma.

                    WILLOW
          It's all over school. What happened
          with Debbie and Pete... Except for
          the "Pete was a monster" part.

                    OZ
          Yeah. A freshman told me that Pete
          had eight iced cafe mochas and lost
          it.

                    BUFFY
          It's better than the estrogen theory.
          I heard he took all his mother's
          birth control pills.

                    CORDELIA
          He didn't? Pete was a monster?
          Where have I been?

                    XANDER
          In your special place, Cor. And
          that's why I adore you.

                    CORDELIA
          So what's the true story? What
          happened?

                                              CONTINUED

47   CONTINUED: 47

                              WILLOW
               Well, we found Pete's lab dairies and
               stuff. Mr. Science was pulling a
               Jeckel/Hyde deal. He was afraid
               Debbie would leave him - so he mixed
               this potion to get super mas macho.

                              BUFFY
               Thing was, after a while, he didn't
               need a potion to turn into the bad
               guy. He got there on the natch.

                              CORDELIA
               So it was like a real killing? He
               wasn't under the influence of
               anything?

                              BUFFY
               Just himself.

Everyone takes this in. Then Buffy spies Scott across the
way.

                              BUFFY (cont'd)
               I'd better...

She moves off toward him.

                              CORDELIA
               Great. Now I'm going to be stuck
               with serious thoughts all day.

Exasperated, she moves off. Xander gives Willow and Oz a
look - then follows her.

ON BUFFY AND SCOTT

Sitting by the fountain together. Scott's in a shocky place.

                              BUFFY
               I don't even know what to say that
               won't sound stupid or obvious.

                              SCOTT
               I've been friends with both of them
               since before we started school...

                              BUFFY
               If there's anything I can do-

                                                            CONTINUED

47   CONTINUED: (2)   47

                         SCOTT
              Thanks. I'll be fine - or...
                    (then)
              It's just... You never really know
              what's going on inside somebody - do
              you? You think if you care about
              them - you know. But you never
              really do.

Off Buffy - his words hitting home.

                                        FADE TO:

48   INT. MANSION - NIGHT   48

CLOSE ON ANGEL

Sleeping fitfully on the ground. Haunted by animal dreams.
A century of suffering.

WIDEN TO INCLUDE

BUFFY

Huddled in the opposite corner, just watching him...

                         BUFFY (V.O.)
              "Night came on, and a full moon rose
              high over the trees, lighting the
              land till it lay bathed in ghostly
              day... And the strain of the
              primitive remained alive and active.
              Faithfulness and devotion, things
              born of fire and roof, were his; yet
              he retained his wildness and
              wiliness. And from the depths of the
              forest - the call still sounded."

                                        BLACK OUT.

              THE END

BUFFY THE VAMPIRE SLAYER

"Homecoming"

Written and Directed By

David Greenwalt

SHOOTING DRAFT

August 31, 1998 (WHITE)
September 2, 1998 (BLUE)
September 3, 1998 (PINK)
September 8, 1998 (YELLOW)
September 11, 1998 (GREEN)

BUFFY THE VAMPIRE SLAYER

"Homecoming"

CAST LIST

```
BUFFY SUMMERS........................... Sarah Michelle Gellar
XANDER HARRIS........................... Nicholas Brendon
RUPERT GILES............................ Anthony S. Head
WILLOW ROSENBERG........................ Alyson Hannigan
CORDELIA CHASE.......................... Charisma Carpenter
ANGEL................................... David Boreanaz
OZ...................................... Seth Green

MR. TRICK............................... K. Todd Freeman
LYLE GORCH.............................. Jeremy Ratchford
FAITH................................... Eliza Dushku
SCOTT................................... Fab Filippo
MAYOR (RICHARD WILKINS III).............
DEPUTY MAYOR (ALLAN FINCH).............. Jack Plotnick
FRAWLEY................................. Billy Maddox
CANDY................................... Lee Everett
KULAK...................................*Chad Stahelski
FREDERICK............................... Jermyn Daube
HANS.................................... Joseph Daube
JONATHAN................................ Danny Strong
DEVON................................... Jason Hall
MS. MORAN............................... Jennifer Hetrick
OLD MAN................................. Ian Abercrombie
MICHELLE................................ Tori McPetrie
```

BUFFY THE VAMPIRE SLAYER

"Homecoming"

SET LIST

INTERIORS

SUNNYDALE HIGH SCHOOL
     LIBRARY
     HALLWAY
     LOUNGE
     CAFETERIA
     CLASSROOM
BRONZE
MANSION
VAN
OLD MAN'S MANSION
MAYOR'S OFFICE
     *OUTSIDE MAYOR'S OFFICE
WILLOW'S BEDROOM
LIMO
DESERTED CABIN

EXTERIORS

SUNNYDALE HIGH SCHOOL
     FOUNTAIN QUAD
     ENGLISH BUILDING
STREET - OUTSIDE SCHOOL
BUFFY'S HOUSE
WOODS
ANOTHER PART OF THE WOODS

BUFFY THE VAMPIRE SLAYER

"Homecoming"

TEASER

1   INT. BRONZE - NIGHT   1

CLOSE ON BUFFY - Staring off, a little distracted.

                    CORDELIA
          I think we should get a limo.

                    XANDER
          A big, expensive limo?

                    WILLOW
          That sounds like fun.

WIDER - BUFFY hangs with Oz, Willow, Cordelia, Xander, Scott.

                    WILLOW (cont'd)
          And it is our last Homecoming dance,
          maybe we should make a big deal.

                    XANDER
          You want to talk fun? Public bus. You
          meet the fun-est people! Back me up
          here, Oz.

                    OZ
          Well, if it's a dollar issue, we
          could all take my van...

                    CORDELIA
          Van? The Homecoming Queen does not
          come to the dance in a van. Use your
          head.

                    XANDER
          Well, technically you haven't been
          elected yet...
                    (off the deadly laser
                     that is her look)
          ...although you most certainly and without
          doubt will.
                    (to the others)
          Who likes a limo?

                                                    CONTINUED

1 CONTINUED: 1

                              WILLOW
                    A private limo...
                              (links her arm
                              through Oz's)
                    ...it is pretty... cuddlesome.
                              (to Buffy)
                    If we all split the cost...

                              BUFFY
                    Maybe, you know, if I go and all...

                              WILLOW
                    Why wouldn't you? You bought your
                    tickets already. I mean unless you
                    didn't have a da --
                              (almost says date)
                    -- ay or two to think it over. We
                    should all think it over.

                              CORDELIA
                    What's going on? Scott hasn't asked
                    her to the Homecoming dance yet?*   *

They all look at Scott.

                              BUFFY
                    Thank you, Cordelia. The
                    humiliation's so good for my color.

                              SCOTT
                    Oh...
                              (to Buffy)
                    No, I just... I sort of assumed you'd
                    think that was corny. But I'm in...
                    you know, I mean if you want to.

                              BUFFY
                    I do. If you do.

                              SCOTT
                    I do. If you do.

Buffy starts to speak again, Oz jumps in:

                              OZ
                    The judges will accept that as a yes.

                                                        CONTINUED

1 CONTINUED: (2)   1

                         BUFFY
                    (to take attention
                    off herself)
               So, Cordy, what's your strategy for
               winning the election? Is it safe to
               say bribes are involved?

                         CORDELIA
               Bribes are only part of it. A year
               ago I would have had this thing sewn.
               But the public's fickle. There's
               competition now, not to mention my
               liabilites.
                    (glances at Xander)

                         XANDER
               Are you saying that dating me is some
               kind of hindrance to you bagging
               Homecoming Queen?

                         CORDELIA
               Oh, sweetie... it's okay, I can
               overcome it, I'm that good.

                         XANDER
               Well, all right then.

     Scott leans in to Buffy.

                         SCOTT
               You want another drink?

                         BUFFY
               You know what? I'm a little tired.
               Think I'll call it a night. I'm
               excited about the Homecoming dance.

     He smiles. She leans in, gives him a pretty nice kiss.

                         BUFFY (cont'd)
               See you tomorrow.

2
     EXT. MANSION - NIGHT - ESTABLISHING - (STOCK)   2

3 INT. MANSION - NIGHT   3

     Fire in fireplace; Angel, in pants, shirt open, edgy and
     restless, paces. He HEARS A SOUND at the French doors.

                                                      CONTINUED

3   CONTINUED: 3

Moves towards them ready to attack, rips the doors open,
scaring:

                    BUFFY
          It's me!

Edgy moment, he backs off, she enters, hands him a bag that
says "Mel's Butcher Shop" on the side. He turns away, pulls
a quart container of blood out of the bag. He holds it to his
nose, scents it, then, aware of Buffy, sets it on a table.

                    BUFFY (cont'd)
          How are you feeling?

                    ANGEL
          It hurts... less.

                    BUFFY
          I haven't told Giles or the others
          you're back...

                    ANGEL
               (remembering)
          Giles...

                    BUFFY
          I'm not going to, they wouldn't
          understand that you're...

Angel picks up the blood, sets it down again, agitated.

                    BUFFY (cont'd)
          ...better. And I'm going to help you
          keep getting better but...
          everything's different now, Angel.
          I'm working harder at school, I'm a
          Senior now, thinking about college --
          also I have a boyfriend.

Angel suddenly moves to her. She doesn't know what he's going
to do. He reaches for her -- very close, she can smell his
bare skin -- he fixes the (twisted) collar on her jacket or
blouse -- turns away again.

                    BUFFY (cont'd)
          His name is Scott. He's a good, solid
          guy. He makes me happy. And that's
          what I need. Someone I can count on.

                                        SMASH CUT TO:

4   EXT. SCHOOL - ENGLISH BUILDING - DAY   4   *

                                                                           *

Buffy and Scott stand by the English building.

                    SCOTT
          I don't think we should see each
          other anymore.

Buffy stares at him, a lost puppy.

                    BUFFY
          You don't? But... when did this
          happen? Where was I?

                    SCOTT
          I like you, I'm just not sure where
          we're going...

                    BUFFY
          Okay, it's too soon to know where
          we're going... but isn't it too soon
          to not go at all?

                    SCOTT
          Buffy, it's just... before we were
          going out you seemed so full of life,
          like a force of nature. Now you seem
          kind of distracted all the time and --

                    BUFFY
          -- no, I know I do that, because my
          life is so... but I'm getting better
          and you're gonna be seeing a drastic
          distraction reduction from here on
          out...
               (nothing from Scott)
          "Drastic distraction reduction", try
          saying that ten times fast."

                    SCOTT
          I'm really sorry.

He goes. Buffy stands there totally stunned. WE PULL BACK
from her, making her a tiny figure, alone in the world.

5   A REALLY LONG LENS SHOT - BINOC MAT - DAY

Of Buffy standing there.

6   EXT. STREET - OUTSIDE SCHOOL - DAY   6

PUSH IN ON A VAN with blacked out windows.

7   INT. VAN - DAY   7

A huge, high tech pair of binocs fills the frame. Two burly
hands lower the binocs, revealing FREDERICK, athletic, Aryan
killer. He looks to his right. CAMERA PANS TO REVEAL his twin
<u>brother</u> HANS next to him: two focussed, methodical, bug-fuck
peas in a pod. Frederick wears an earwig. The van's full of
high-tech surveillance equipment, etc. Hans plugs a wire into
the binocs as Frederick raises them to his eyes again. CAMERA
FOLLOWS the wire to a cellular modem hook-up. CAMERA PUSHES
IN ON MODEM.

8   INT. OLD MAN'S MANSION - DAY   8

MATCH CUT TO A SIMILAR MODEM, follow the wire to a high tech
computer monitor.

Dark and gloomy in here. Wood, tapestries, wealth. A sullen,
craggy figure sits hunched in a wheelchair before a high tech
computer monitor. On the Monitor we see the <u>binoc-matted shot
of Buffy</u> looking lost and alone. The OLD MAN types, the shot
of Buffy enlarges.

                    OLD MAN
            Is that her?

Mr. Trick walks into frame.

                    MR. TRICK
            In the nubile flesh, my friend.

PUSHING IN on Buffy's image --

                    MR. TRICK (O.S.)
            That's the target.

                                        BLACK OUT.

                    END OF TEASER

ACT ONE

9 EXT. SCHOOL - DAY - ESTABLISHING (STOCK)   9

10 INT. SCHOOL LOUNGE - DAY   10

CORDELIA smiles into camera. FLASH! FREEZE FRAME, then:

XANDER sits -- big dorky smile. FLASH!

WILLOW smiles shyly -- then looks worried, nothing
happening -- and FLASH!

OZ -- no expression. FLASH!

A PHOTOGRAPHER is taking class pictures, kids lined up near
a stand with various types and sample sizes of school pics.

Xander and Willow walk across the room as Oz is still being   *
photographed.   *

                    WILLOW   *
          You have to help me pick an outfit.   *
          I wanna wear something that'll make   *
          Oz go "ooh."   *

                    XANDER   *
          No problem. I got the tux goin' on,   *
          I'm gonna look hot if it even   *
          remotely fits.   *

They approach Cordy, who is eyeing someone.   *

                    XANDER (cont'd)
          Whatchya doin'?

                    CORDELIA
          Checking out the I laughingly use the
          phrase competition.

She indicates two PRETTY GIRLS, HOLLY and MICHELLE, talking   *
to groups of students nearby.

                    CORDELIA (cont'd)
          Holly Charlston, nice girl, brain-
          dead, doesn't have a prayer...
                    (more)

                                                    CONTINUED

10   CONTINUED: 10

                         CORDELIA (cont'd)
                    and Michelle Blake, open to all
                    mankind, especially if they have a
                    letterman's jacket and a car -- she
                    could give me a run.

Oz joins them.   *

                         WILLOW
                    Where's Buffy? She's going to miss
                    the yearbook pictures.

                         XANDER
                    She and Faith are in the library,
                    getting sweaty.

                         CORDELIA
                    They're <u>training</u>.

                         XANDER
                    I stand by my phrase.

                         OZ
                    I don't think she was here the day
                    they announced 'em. Did anybody tell
                    her?

                         CORDELIA
                    I'll tell her now. I've gotta go by
                    the Nurse's office and get an ice
                    pack.

                         XANDER
                    Did you hurt yourself?

                         CORDELIA
                    No silly...
                         (pats her face)
                    ...shrinks the pores.

11   INT. LIBRARY - DAY   11

BUFFY punches right at CAMERA! She and Faith spar, hard. A
last solid hit from Buffy and they stop, breathing hard and
sweating.

                         FAITH
                    Man. Guys should break up with you
                    more often.

                                                            CONTINUED

11   CONTINUED: 11

                    BUFFY
          Gee. Thanks.

                    FAITH
          I mean it. You've got some quality rage
          going. Really gives you an edge.

                    BUFFY
          Lucky me. Edge girl.

The drink Gatorade and towel off, sitting as they talk,
Buffy stretching out a bit.

                    FAITH   *
          Well, screw him. You move on, you
          party -- heavily -- you'll be fine.
          You're still going to that dance,
          right?

                    BUFFY
          I don't know...

                    FAITH
          You got the tix already... Why don't
          we go together?

                    BUFFY
               (considering it)
          Well, maybe...

                    FAITH
          Come on, we'll find a couple a studs,
          use 'em and discard 'em like old
          hankies. That's <u>always</u> fun.

                    BUFFY
          Okay. I'm on. Not the stud-using
          part -- or, probably not...

12   INT. SCHOOL HALL - DAY   12

Cor moves up, looks through the little round windows into the
library, sees Buffy and Faith. She's about to enter when TWO
GUYS move past behind her.

                    CORDELIA
          Bobby, Mashad, you don't phone, you
          don't write...
                    (heads off after them)
          ...I miss you guys, seriously...

13   EXT. SUNNYDALE CITY HALL - DAY - (STOCK)   13

American flag flies in front of the quaint tower of power.

A14 INT. OUTSIDE MAYOR'S OFFICE - DAY   A14   *

Deputy Mayor ALLAN FINCH stands nervously outside the office,   *
waiting. He holds a manila file folder under one arm. A   *
SECRETARY types impassively next to him.   *

CLOSE ON ALLAN   *

He jumps slightly as the secretary's buzzer goes off.   *

                    SECRETARY (O.S.)
          The Mayor will see you now.   *

14   INT. MAYOR'S OFFICE - CONTINUOUS - DAY   14   *

Finch opens the doors and enters, stopping as the mayor   *
passes before him, wiping his hands (which are all we see of   *
him in frame) on a paper towel. Allan's eyes follow the   *
mayor to his desk.

                    FINCH
          I'm sorry to bother you, sir.   *

                    MAYOR (O.S.)
          I'm not bothered, Allan.   *

                    FINCH
                    (crossing to the desk)
          Well, I'm not sure how serious this   *
          is, sir. But they were spotted in   *
          town three days ago. I've just been   *
          informed.   *

                                                  CONTINUED

14 CONTINUED: 14

He places a photo on the mayor's desk. The two twins who   *
were spying on Buffy.   *

                    FINCH (cont'd)   *
          Frederick and Hans Gruenshtahler.   *
          Wanted in Germany for capital murder,   *
          terrorism, the bombing of flight   *
          1402...

As Allan talks, the mayor takes the picture and we get our   *
first good look at his face. It couldn't be more unassuming.   *
One feels this man has not raised his voice in years, and   *
although he is mild enough in demeanor, one hopes he won't.   *

He looks carefully at the picture and as Allan continues to   *
talk, he rather pensively SNIFFS it.   *

                    FINCH (cont'd)
          I should have brought it to your   *
          attention sooner, but I wanted to   *
          confirm...   *

He stops, unnerved by the sniffing.   *

                    MAYOR
          Would you show me your hands, please?   *

                    FINCH
          Sir?   *

                    MAYOR
          Your hands.   *

He indicates the desk top. Slowly, Allan puts his hand down   *
flat on the desk. He is clearly terrified now. The mayor   *
looks at him, his own hand mere inches from a sharp looking   *
letter opener. After a beat of scrutiny, he looks up at Allan.   *

                    MAYOR (cont'd)
          I think they could be cleaner.   *

                    FINCH
          Of course, sir, I mean I washed them,   *
          but --   *

                    FINCH (cont'd)
          Yes sir.   *

                                                        CONTINUED

                              243

14   CONTINUED: (2)   14

                         MAYOR
              After every meal, and under the   *
              fingernails. Dirt gets trapped   *
              there. And germs. And mayonnaise.   *

                         FINCH
              Yes sir.   *

                                             CONTINUED

14   CONTINUED: (3)   14

                          MAYOR
              My dear mother said that cleanliness   *
              was next to godliness and I believed   *
              her. She never caught a cold.   *
                      (closing the folder)   *
              I'd like these two to be put under   *
              surveillance. And I'd like to know   *
              if any other colorful characters have   *
              come to town.   *

                          FINCH
              I'll take care of it.   *

                          MAYOR
              You have all my faith.   *

       A moment, and the deputy mayor turns and goes, visibly   *
       sweating.   *

15   INT. WILLOW'S BEDROOM - NIGHT   15

       Willow, in a slip, has a slew of clothes laid out on the bed.
       She picks up a sweater (or blouse, Cynthia), holds it in
       front of her, leans around a standing screen that separates
       her from Xander, in tux pants, white shirt, trying to tie a
       bow tie.

                          WILLOW
              What do you think of this?

                          XANDER
              Nice.

       Willow nods, drops it on the bed, picks up something else.

                          WILLOW
              It's my first big dance, you know,
              where there's a boy and a band and
              not just me alone in my room
              pretending there's a boy and a band,
              so I want it to be...

                          XANDER
              ...special. Which is why I spared no
              expense on the tux.

                          WILLOW
              I thought you borrowed it from your
              cousin Rigby.

                                                          CONTINUED

15   CONTINUED: 15

                    XANDER
          Expense to my pride, Will. They're
          our only relations with money and
          they shun us, as they should.

Willow leans around the screen again.

                    WILLOW
          What do you think of this?

                    XANDER
          Nice.

Willow nods, fixes Xander's bow tie for him. She looks at him.

                    XANDER (cont'd)
          What?

                    WILLOW
          I was just... remember the eighth
          grade cotillion? You had that clip-
          on...

                    XANDER
          I was stylin' with the clip-on.

                    WILLOW
          And now here we are, it's Homecoming.

                    XANDER
          Face it, Will. You and I are gonna
          be in neighboring rest homes, and I'm
          gonna be stopping by to have you
          adjust my... my... I can't think of
          anything that's not really gross.

Willow smiles, finishes the tie, goes back to the bed where
she will be putting on a dress (we won't see much of) as:

                    XANDER (cont'd)
          So, uh, you and Oz, how can I put
          this... are we on first, second or,
          yee gods.

                    WILLOW
          That is none of your business,
          Alexander Harris.

                                                CONTINUED

15 CONTINUED: (2)   15

                    XANDER
                (impressed)
        Oh, rounding second.

                    WILLOW
        You don't know that, what about you
        and Cordelia?

Xander slips on his tux coat.

                    XANDER
        A gentleman never talks about his
        conquests.

                    WILLOW
        Since when did you become a --

Willow steps around the screen in a stunning dress. Looks at
Xander in full tux: James Bond meets God.

                    WILLOW (cont'd)
        -- gentleman.

He just stares at her for a long moment. She looks down at
her own outfit.

                    WILLOW (cont'd)
        I know. "Nice."

                    XANDER
                (sincerely)
        I was gonna go with "gorgeous."

                    WILLOW
        Really?
                (nods)
        You, too. In a guy way.

                    XANDER
        Oz is very lucky.

                    WILLOW
        So is Cordelia -- in a girl way.

Beat. They don't quite know what to say.

                    WILLOW (cont'd)
        I don't know if I can dance in this.
                (thinks)
        I don't know if I can dance...

                                              CONTINUED

15   CONTINUED: (3)   15

                          XANDER
              Come on, piece of cake. Here.

He takes her in his arms. They dance a little, getting
closer, looking at one another.

                          XANDER (cont'd)
              That seems to...

                          WILLOW
              Yeah, it shouldn't be a...
                      (they get even closer)
              ...problem.

                          XANDER
              No... no problem...

And now they're very close; and then, gently, they're
kissing. Then a little more than gently. Then they both pull
back at the same instant.

                          XANDER (cont'd)
              That didn't just happen.

                          WILLOW
              No. I mean it did but it didn't.

                          XANDER
              Because I respect you -- and Oz --
              and I would never --

                          WILLOW
              I wouldn't ever, either. It's the
              clothes. It's a fluke.

                          XANDER
              It's a clothes fluke, and that's what
              it is and there'll be no more fluking.

                          WILLOW
              Not ever.

Beat. They look like they might kiss again, then --

                          XANDER
              We got to get out of these clothes.

                          WILLOW
              Right now!

                                                              CONTINUED

15   CONTINUED: (4)   15

                         XANDER
              Oh, I didn't mean --

                         WILLOW
              Me, either!

They run for opposite sides of the screen.

16   EXT. SCHOOL - FOUNTAIN QUAD - DAY   16   *

Buffy moves between classes. Sees a kindly looking TEACHER.

                         BUFFY
              Ms. Moran, I'm so glad I ran into
              you. I had a little incident last
              year of... getting kicked out of
              school. I'm back, I've done all my
              make-ups but I still need one written
              recommendation from a teacher -- I
              think the word Principal Snyder used
              was "glowing" -- for my file, to show
              I belong here.

                         MS. MORAN
              And you are...?

                         BUFFY
              Buffy. Buffy Summers, second row,
              third from the front in your class...
                   (Moran shrugs)
              ..."Contemporary American Heros:
              From Amelia Earhart to Maya Angelou",
              the class that changed my life?

                         MS. MORAN
              Were you absent a lot, uh...

                         BUFFY
              Buffy.

Off Buffy,

17   INT. CAFETERIA - DAY   17

A FLYER - is thrust at CAMERA. Cordelia's pic, her million
dollar smile and the words "You Get More With Cor" emblazoned
across it.

                                                        CONTINUED

17 CONTINUED: 17

PAN TO CORDELIA - handing out flyers

                        CORDELIA
                Hi. I hope you'll consider me for
                Homecoming Queen...

ANGLE - A TABLE

Oz, Willow, Xander and Buffy lunch. Xander and Willow are
consumed with silent guilt. Buffy's a little down.

                        BUFFY
                I can't believe it. My favorite
                teacher and she didn't remember me.
                I'm like a non-person. Am I turning
                invisible?
                        (to Oz)
                Can you see me?

                        OZ
                Big as life.

                        BUFFY
                At Hemery I was Prom Queen, Fiesta
                Queen, I was on the cheerleading
                squad -- the yearbook was, like, a
                story of me. Now it's senior year
                and I'm gonna be one crappy picture
                on one eighth of one crappy page.

                        XANDER
                Uh, no, actually, you're not.

                        BUFFY
                What do you mean?

                        XANDER
                Well, you missed the picture taking.

                        BUFFY
                When? Why?

                        OZ
                We did 'em yesterday.

                        WILLOW
                Didn't Cordelia tell you?

Off Buffy,

                                                    CONTINUED

17 CONTINUED: (2)   17

CORDELIA HANDS OUT FLYER -- BUFFY STEPS IN FRONT OF HER

                    CORDELIA
          Buffy, you look so adorable in that --

                    BUFFY
          I'm not voting for you.

                    CORDELIA
          Then make it snappy.

                    BUFFY
          Why didn't you tell me they were
          doing the yearbook pictures?

                    CORDELIA
          Didn't I? Guess I forgot. What's the
          big?

                    BUFFY
          The big is that it's the yearbook!
          It's the book about... the year!

                    CORDELIA
          Yeah, hence the name.

                    BUFFY
          You just could have thought about
          someone else for thirty seconds,
          that's all.

                    CORDELIA
          Hey, I'm under a lot of pressure here.

                    BUFFY
          Oh, yeah, Homecoming campaign. Rough
          gig.

                    CORDELIA
          What would you know about it? Just
          because you were Guacamole Queen when
          you were three doesn't mean you
          understand how this works.

                    BUFFY
          Yeah, appparently it involves handing
          out these entirely lame flyers.

                                          CONTINUED

17   CONTINUED: (3)   17

                        CORDELIA
            No, it involves being a part of the
            school and having actual friends.
            Now if it was about monsters and
            blood and innards, you'd be a shoo in.

It's safe to say she's gone too far. She sees it, too, but
can't back down. She starts past a glaring Buffy, muttering:

                        CORDELIA (cont'd)
            Like to see you try to win the crown.

Buffy watches her start to leave.

                        BUFFY
            Oh, you would?

Cordy turns back.

                        BUFFY (cont'd)
            Then you will.

                        CORDELIA
            What do you mean?

                        BUFFY
            I'll show you how it's done. I'll go
            for Homecoming Queen and I'll win.

                        CORDELIA
            This is starting to be sad.

                        BUFFY
            Sorry, Cordy, but you have no idea
            who you're messing with.

                        CORDELIA
            What, the Slayer?

                        BUFFY
            I'm not talking about the Slayer.
            I'm talking about Buffy. You've
            awakened the Prom Queen within,
            Cordy. And that crown is gonna be
            mine.

The stare at each other.

                        MR. TRICK (V.O)
            Competition.

18 INT. OLD MAN'S MANSION - NIGHT   18

                    MR. TRICK
          Competition is a beautiful thing.
          Makes us strive. Makes us
          accomplish. Occasionally makes us
          kill.

Mr. Trick lectures the assembled killers. They include:
Frederick and Hans (with AR-15 semi-automatic rifles, laser
sight, grenade); the old man at his computer terminal;
FRAWLEY, a leathery big game hunter; KULAK, a demon, yellow   *
skin, yellow eyes, dinosaur spines across his bald head;
Texas vampire LYLE GORCH and his bride CANDY, pink barrette
in her hair.

                    MR. TRICK (cont'd)
          We all feel the desire to win,
          whether we're human...
                    (indicates the humans)
          ...vampire...
                    (indicates the
                    Gorches)
          ...Or...
                    (Kulak)
          ...whatever the hell you are, my
          brother, got them spiny looking head
          things, I never seen that.

                    KULAK
          I am Kulak, of the Miquot clan.

                    MR. TRICK
          Isn't that nice. Point is, you're
          all here for one reason.

                    GORCH
          Well, it wasn't for no philosophy
          class.

                    MR. TRICK
          Mr. Gorch. My account statement
          shows your deposit has yet to be made.

Gorch dumps a sack of money -- stacks of bloody hundreds --
on the table.

                    GORCH
          Me and Candy's blowing our whole
          honeymoon stash on this little game.

                                             CONTINUED

18   CONTINUED: 18

                         MR. TRICK
              They're dirty.

                         GORCH
              They're non-consecutive.

         Trick considers, then shrugs.

                         MR. TRICK
              In a few days time, the game will
              commence. You will all have the
              opportunity to bring down not one but
              two of the toughest prize bucks this
              world has to offer. The first
              target, Buffy, you've all seen. The
              second, Faith, is more elusive, but
              both targets will be together and
              ready for the killing and that's a
              money-back guarantee. Ladies,
              Gentlemen, and spiny-headed lookin'
              creatures... welcome to SlayerFest.
              Ninety eight.

                                        BLACK OUT.

                         END OF ACT ONE

ACT TWO

19   EXT. SCHOOL - DAY - ESTABLISHING (STOCK)   19

                       BUFFY (O.S.)
              A campaign is like a war...

20   INT. SCHOOL - LIBRARY - DAY   20

     Buffy, with sketches, time tables, a white board and pointer
     (listing the other candidates, their strengths and
     weaknesses), presents battle plans to Willow and Xander
     (looking guilty) and Oz. She is excited and in her element.
     Giles watches in b.g.

                       BUFFY
              ...it's won or lost in the trenches.
              Holly, Michelle...
                       (hits board with
                       pointer on each name)
              ...and our real competition,
              Cordelia, all have a big head   *
              start -- speaking of Cordelia's head,   *
              if I had a watermelon that big, I'd   *
              be rich!

     Nothing from Xander, Will and Oz.   *

                       BUFFY (cont'd)
              -- waits for laugh... right, don't   *
              rag on the competition, makes me look   *
              petty. Anyway, I've done this   *
              before, it's just like any other   *
              popularity contest -- the only   *
              difference being that this time I'm   *
              not actually popular. But I'm not
              unpopular, exactly. I mean, a lot of
              people came to my welcome home party.

                       WILLOW
              But they were killed by zombies.

                       BUFFY
              Good point. Will, I want you to set
              up a database, who's for us, who's on
              the fence, crisis areas. Oz, you
              take the fringe, musicians, not
              inclined to vote, could be an
              important swing. Xander --

                                                CONTINUED

20 CONTINUED: 20

Cordelia enters. An awkward beat.

                    BUFFY (cont'd)
          Hi Cordelia. I know this is kinda
          awkward but I don't see why we can't
          all get along during the campaign.
          We're all buds, we're all going to
          the dance together in the limo.

                    CORDELIA
          Great.
                    (to Willow)
          How's the database coming?

You thought Willow looked guilty before?

                    WILLOW
          Uh... it's... just about done.

                    CORDELIA
          Xander?

                    XANDER
          I've got your new flyers...

                    CORDELIA
          Let's get cracking.

Xander, Willow and Oz move to Cordelia's side of the room.

                    XANDER
                    (to Buffy)
          She's my girlfriend.

                    WILLOW
                    (to Buffy)
          It's just... she needs it so much
          more than you do.

                    OZ
          As Willow goes so goes my nation.

                    CORDELIA
          Thanks for what you said, Buffy. I
          think we're getting along good, don't
          you?

She turns and goes. The rest follow her like guilty dogs.
Buffy picks up her Snapple (or similar glass bottled drink)
and sips as Giles moves up.

                                              CONTINUED

20 CONTINUED: (2)   20

                         GILES
               Seems like an awful lot of fuss for a
               little title.

                         BUFFY
               Giles, it's no fun if you don't try
               your best.

                         GILES
               As long as fun is still in the mix...

                         BUFFY
               Sure. It's not like anyone takes it
               <u>that</u> seriously.

     INSERT: BUFFY'S HAND

     As it actually <u>crushes</u> the Snapple bottle.

     Buffy smiles guilelessly at Giles.   (While Miles files piles
     of tiles.) (I'm very sorry.)

     <u>MONTAGE:</u> MUSIC UP

21   EXT. SCHOOL - FOUNTAIN QUAD - DAY   21

     Buffy chats (M.O.S.) with a group of STUDENTS. Laughing,
     charming, touching a guy on the arm. We STEADI CAM PAST HER
     and discover Cordelia doing the same thing down stream.

22
     INT. OLD MAN'S MANSION - DAY   22   *

     Frawley checks the action in his 30 aught 6. PAN TO Frederick
     and Hans, doing bare-chested knuckle push-ups on the floor.
     PAN TO Gorch and Candy, necking.

23
     INT. SCHOOL - LOUNGE - DAY   23   *

     Homecoming Queen posters on the board, including HOLLY
     CHARLESTON'S and MICHELLE BLAKE'S. PANNING ACROSS Cordelia's
     poster we find Buffy pinning up one of her own. Unlike the
     others, it's hip, Dutch-angled and M.T.V. colored.   *

24 INT. OLD MAN'S MANSION - NIGHT   24

Frederick and Hans fight hand to hand; PAN To the old man at
his computer running map grids of the city; PAN To Kulak. He
takes a deep breath and cocks his arms, wrist to shoulder.
He straightens them and two (CGI) blades come out of his
forearms, fly into his hands. He HURLS ONE OF HIS BLADES.

A TARGET NEXT TO GORCH AND CANDY, NECKING, SHATTERS!

                    GORCH
          Hey, Swiss Army Knife -- wanna reign
          it in a little?

                    CANDY
          Sugar, everyone else's got weapons
          and plans, shouldn't we be...?

                    GORCH
          Don't worry, I got a plan. You
          ferget, I'm the only one in this game
          actually knows the Slayer, what
          she'll do.

                    CANDY
          You are just a big, strong, manly
          cowboy and I love you.

                    GORCH
          Gimme that sugar.

They neck. Pan to Frawley setting a mannequin leg in one of   *
his bear traps -- it snaps the leg in two.   *

25 EXT. SCHOOL - FOUNTAIN QUAD - DAY   25 *

Buffy drops a bunch of flyers, wearily stoops to pick them
up. Scott is passing, bends down to help.

                    SCOTT
          Here.

                    BUFFY
               (awkwardly)
          Oh. Thanks.

                    SCOTT
               (looking at flyer)
          I heard you were doing this.

                                              CONTINUED

25 CONTINUED: 25

                         BUFFY
            It's just something to fill the time,
            it's kind of silly, really.

                         SCOTT
            I don't think so. For what it's
            worth, you've got my vote.

                         BUFFY
            I really don't want to --
                    (stops herself)
            Thank you.

He nods a little self-consciously, moves off. She drops the
sad girl act, whips out a LIST - checks off SCOTT HOPE.

26 EXT. SCHOOL - DAY   26   *

Holly talks to a kid, gives him a cookie. As his hand is
about to take it, Buffy puts a cupcake in it.

27 EXT. SCHOOL - DAY   27

Two other kids eat Buffy's cupcakes, their mouths chocolatey.
Cordelia walks up, gives each of them a small dessert basket.

28 INT. SCHOOL - DAY   28

Holly puts her poster up. CUT: Michelle takes it down, puts
up her own poster. CUT: Cordelia takes it down, puts up her
poster. CUT: The words "Get More With Cor" on Cor's poster as
Buffy tags them: "Get Bored With Cor".

29 EXT. SCHOOL - DAY   29

Buffy talks and laughs with a "hip" group. CUT: Buffy talks
and laughs with a "jock" group. CUT: Buffy talks and laughs
too hard with a "nerd" group. The nerds look at each other:
this chick is a bigger nerd than they are.

30 INT. SCHOOL - LOUNGE - DAY   30   *

Willow, looking very anxious, walks past a wall of posters.
She looks from Cordelia's to Buffy's, miserable, then sees
BUFFY HERSELF, heading her way. Trapped.

                                                      CONTINUED

30 CONTINUED: 30

                         BUFFY
               Hi.

                         WILLOW
               Oh hi. How are you? You good? You
               look good. And what else is new with
               you? Did I mention you look --

                         BUFFY
               Will, it's okay, you helping
               Cordelia. You're my friend, I'm not
               going to hold it against you.

                         WILLOW
               No, I'm not a friend, I'm a rabid dog
               who should be shot but there are
               forces at work here, dark
               incomprehensible forces...

                         BUFFY
               And I'm sure they're more important
               than all we've been through together
               or how many times I've saved your
               life...

                         WILLOW
                    (tiny voice)
               What do you want?

                         BUFFY
               Fifteen minutes alone on your
               computer with Cordelia's data base.

                         WILLOW
                    (tinier voice)
               'Kay.

     They move off, Buffy quite chipper.

                         BUFFY
               So I called the limo place and we're
               all set. It's gonna swing by
               Faith's, then my place...

31 INT. VAN - DAY   31

     Frederick and Hans have a listening mic pointed at school.

                                                         CONTINUED

31 CONTINUED: 31

                         BUFFY (O.S., FILTERED)
                    ...and then your house, unless you're
                    gonna be at Oz', and then...

32 INT. SCHOOL LOUNGE - DAY   32

    Buffy gives Jonathan a cupcake. He munches as:

                         BUFFY
                    You know Jonathan, I've always felt
                    a special bond between you and me --

                         JONATHAN
                    Cordelia gave me six bucks. That
                    buys a whole lotta cupcakes.

                         BUFFY
                    Okay, how 'bout... you vote for me
                    and I don't beat the living crap out
                    of you.

    Jonathan stops chewing, swallows.

                         JONATHAN
                    That works good for me.
                         (backs away)

                         BUFFY
                         (cheery)
                    Tell your friends!

    Buffy looks:

INTO THE UPPER LOUNGE

Where Cordelia laughs loudly with a group of EXTREME NERDS.

                         CORDELIA
                    Are you kidding? I've been doing the
                    Vulcan death grip since I was four!

    She does it wrong, then tries to do it like the five nerds
    are doing it as Buffy marches up.

                         BUFFY
                    You're giving out money now?

                                                          CONTINUED

32   CONTINUED: 32

                         CORDELIA
              So? Is that any more tacky than your
              faux "I'm shy but deep" campaign
              posters?

                         BUFFY
              Yes.

                         CORDELIA
              This whole trying to be like me
              really isn't funny anymore.

                         BUFFY
              I was never trying to be like you and
              when was it funny?

                         CORDELIA
              I don't see why your pathetic need to
              recapture your glory days gives you
              the right to splinter my vote!

                         BUFFY
               How can you think it's okay to talk
              to people like that? Do you have
              parents?

                         CORDELIA
              Yeah. <u>Two</u> of them. Unlike some
              people.

                         BUFFY
               Your brain isn't even connected to
              your mouth. Is it?

                         CORDELIA
              Why don't you do us both a favor and
              stay out of my way?

Cordelia brushes -- or rather tries to brush -- Buffy aside.
Buffy catches her hand.

                         BUFFY
               Don't ever do that again.

                         CORDELIA
              You're sick, you know that?

Xander (arriving with Willow) grabs Cordelia.

                                        CONTINUED

32 CONTINUED: (2)   32

                    XANDER
          Okay, let's not say things we'll
          regret later --

                    CORDELIA
          Crazy freak!

                    BUFFY
          Vapid whore!

                    XANDER
          -- like that.

Xander pulls Cordy away. Willow looks at Buffy:

                    WILLOW
          This is just --

33 INT. WILLOW'S BEDROOM - DAY   33

                    WILLOW
          -- the worst thing that's ever
          happened.

Xander and Willow alone, wigged.

                    XANDER
          I know, I know, but when I look at
          you now...
                    (puts his hands on
                     her shoulders)
          ...it's like I'm seeing you for the
          first time, I know it's crazy but I
          can't help it.

                    WILLOW
          I'm talking about Buffy and Cordelia.

                    XANDER
                    (drops his hands)
          Me too.

                    WILLOW
          What are we gonna do? We have to do
          something. This is all our fault.

                    XANDER
          How do you get from chick fight to
          "our fault"?

                                              CONTINUED

33   CONTINUED: 33

                              WILLOW
                Because, we felt so guilty about the
                fluke, we went overboard helping
                Cordelia -- and spun the whole group
                dynamic out of orbit -- we're a
                meteor storm heading for earth!

                              XANDER
                Okay, calm down, let's put our heads
                together and think of something. One
                of us is pretty darn smart and I'm...
                just in hell. I thought being a
                Senior -- at last -- and having a
                girlfriend -- at last -- would be a
                good thing. Shouldn't that be a good
                thing?
                        (she smiles)
                What?

                              WILLOW
                Sometimes when you're falling apart
                your mouth does the sweetest thing.

                              XANDER
                My mouth?

Willow touches his mouth. He touches her hand. They come
together and just hold onto one another. No kissage.

                              WILLOW
                What are we gonna do?

                              XANDER
                We just gotta get the two of them
                communicating.

                              WILLOW
                I'm talking about us.

34   EXT. BUFFY'S HOUSE - NIGHT   34

Buffy, in prom dress, heads down the walk to a waiting limo.
The uniformed driver (whose face we won't see) holds the door
for her. As she gets in:

35   INT. LIMO - NIGHT   35

Buffy sits, sees Cordelia, also in prom dress (and corsage).

                                                        CONTINUED

35   CONTINUED: 35

                         BUFFY
              What are you doing here?   Where's
              Faith?

Cordelia icily hands Buffy a note. Buffy reads:

                         BUFFY (cont'd)
              "Dear Cordelia and Buffy, we won't be
              riding to the dance with you. We want
              you to work out your problems because
              our friendships are more important
              than who wins Homecoming Queen. Your
              friends. P.S., the limo was not
              cheap, work it out."
                         (beat)
              Well...

She sees two corsage boxes, one empty.

                         BUFFY (cont'd)
              They gave us corsages?

                         CORDELIA
              I took the orchid.

                         BUFFY
              Oh.
                         (takes out other
                          corsage, pins it to
                          her dress)
              Nice of you to check with me on that.

Cordelia gives her a bitchy look.

36   EXT. BUFFY'S HOUSE - NIGHT - THE DRIVER   36

Starts the car. We see that it is FREDERICK. The limo pulls
away.

                                             DISSOLVE TO:

37   EXT. ROAD LEADING FROM CITY TO COUNTRY - NIGHT - STOCK   37

Only if we can find this in STOCK FOOTAGE. A black limo
leaves suburbia -- or a black limo on a country road -- or a
black limo heading into a woodsy locale.

                                             DISSOLVE TO:

38   INT. LIMO - NIGHT - POOR MAN'S   38

                          CORDELIA
            I don't see what the big deal is.

                          BUFFY
            I'm not making a big deal. You wanted
            the orchid, you took the orchid.

                          CORDELIA
            It goes with my complexion better.

                          BUFFY
            It does have a sallow tint...
                    (limo stops)
            Finally, we're here.

      They hear the driver's door open and shut. Then footsteps
      like he's running away. Off Buffy,

39   EXT. WOODS - NIGHT   39

      Buffy and Cordy get out, look around.

                          CORDELIA
            What is this?
                    (calls out)
            Okay, guys, we've had enough of
            your stupid games.

                          BUFFY
            What's massively wrong with this
            picture?

      Cordelia follows Buffy's gaze to A BIG T.V. Sitting there in
      the woods. They move to it. A big post-it note says "Press
      Power, then Play". Buffy does. The (battery-operated) T.V.
      clicks on and we see and we see Mr. Trick on V.H.S.

                          MR. TRICK
            Hello ladies, welcome to SlayerFest
            ninety-eight. What is a SlayerFest
            you ask? Well, as in most of life,
            there's the hunters and the hunted.
            Can you guess where you two fall? You
            have exactly thirty seconds from the
            beginning of this tape --
                    (checks watch)
            -- oo, seventeen now -- to run for
            your lives. Faith, Buffy, have a nice
            death.

                                                      CONTINUED

39   CONTINUED: 39

The tape ends. Buffy does a three sixty, scanning the woods
for danger. Cordy just stares at the T.V., irritated.

                         CORDELIA
              Hello, how stupid are you people.
              She's a Slayer, I am a Homecoming
              Quee--

Suddenly a bullet shatters the TV, blowing it to bits.
Cordelia screams bloody murder. Buffy grabs Cordelia and they
run like hell into the woods.

                                        BLACK OUT.

                    END OF ACT TWO

ACT THREE

40   INT. BRONZE - NIGHT   40

Oz' band plays an upbeat love song. Place is decked out for
Homecoming, banners, refreshment table, etc. FIND WILLOW AND
XANDER standing rather far apart. Faith walks up between
them, wearing her own high fashion statement.

                    FAITH
          What are you two so mopey about?

                    XANDER
          We're not mopey. We're grooving. On
          Oz' band. He's a wonderful guy, Oz.

                    WILLOW
                 (verge of tears)
          He wrote this song for me.

Faith gives them a look, sees Scott with a date.

                    FAITH
          That sleazebag...

Giles moves up, alarmed.

                    GILES
          We've got to find Buffy. Something
          terrible's happened.
                 (off their looks)
          Just kidding. Thought I'd give you
          a scare. Are those finger sandwiches?

He heads for refreshment table --

                    XANDER
          Giles is developing a sense of humor.

                    WILLOW
          I'm scared, too.

41   EXT. WOODS - NIGHT   41

ON THE GROUND - Two pairs of dress shoes run. NORMAL ANGLE -
Buffy grabs Cordy, pulls her off the path into the trees.

                    BUFFY
          We gotta get off this path...

                                                      CONTINUED

41   CONTINUED: 41

They keep moving, Buffy looking for danger.

                    CORDELIA
          I have an idea: we talk to these
          people, we explain I'm not a slayer,
          they let me go... LOOK OUT!

Too late. Buffy, looking everywhere but down, has stepped
into one of Frawley's bear traps.

SFX - Probably slo mo - the trap snaps up. Buffy, with slayer
speed, whips her foot back out of the trap.

The trap snaps shut <u>just below</u> Buffy's foot.

Frawley rises out of the darkness, his gun aimed at her.

Buffy dives as Frawley shoots and misses -- Buffy rolls,
whips the trap out of the ground and flings it.

The trap hits Frawley in the head; he staggers back.

Frawley's booted foot steps in one of his own traps. He howls
in incredible pain and falls against a tree.

Buffy grabs his gun, goes to him. Cordy moves up behind
Buffy.

                    BUFFY
          That's gotta smart. Now, I can let
          you out of that trap or I can put a
          bullet in your head. How many are
          there in this little game and what
          are they packing?

Frawley looks at her. He's in incredible pain but he doesn't
say anything -- until she works the action on the 30 aught 6
and drops a shell in.

                    FRAWLEY
          There's me, two Germans with AR-15's   *
          and grenade launcher, yellow-skin   *
          demon with long knives, vampire
          couple from Texas named Gorch.

                    BUFFY
          That everybody?

                                                 CONTINUED

41   CONTINUED: (2)   41

                        FRAWLEY
            Everybody who's out here. Germans are
            wired -- their boss is tracking them
            on computer. Now get me out of this!

                        BUFFY
            Tell you what. If I live, I'll send
            the S.P.C.A. for you. And if I ever
            see you again, I'll kill you where
            you lean.

                        CORDELIA
            Could you do me an eensy favor? Tell
            your friends that I'm not --

Buffy slaps a hand over Cordy's mouth, sensing danger. Buffy
spins around, bringing the gun up. Kulak is behind them,
blades in each hand. He flings one, Buffy shoots.

The blade misses Buffy, sinks in a tree next to her. The
bullet KNOCKS KULAK back and down. Cordelia screams. Buffy
grabs her and they run.

42   INT. BRONZE - NIGHT   42

Scott dances with an extra. Faith moves up.

                        FAITH
            Scott, there you are, Honey. Good
            news -- doctor says the itching and
            the swelling and the burning should
            clear up, but we gotta keep using the
            ointment.
                     (to his date, nice)
            Hi.

Giles moves to Xander and Willow, much less jovial than
before:

                        GILES
            I suspect these finger sandwiches
            contain actual finger. I think I'll
            retreat to the library until the
            coronation, I want to be here when
            Buffy... however it turns out for
            her -- and that was a fine thing you
            two did putting Buffy and Cordelia
            together.
                     (he goes)

                                                        CONTINUED

42 CONTINUED: 42

                        WILLOW
              We did one fine thing.

                        XANDER
              Yeah. They've been gone a while, they
              must really be getting into it.

43 INT. DESERTED CABIN - NIGHT   43

Buffy (gun in hand) kicks the door open. She and Cordy tumble
in. Buffy shuts the door, wedges a chair under the handle.

                        BUFFY
              We're safe for the time being, look
              for a weapon.

Buffy shutters the first window shut, draws a curtain across
it. Cordy hyperventilates.

                        CORDELIA
              Safe? I'm not safe, I'm going to die.

                        BUFFY
              You are if you just stand there.

Buffy moves to the second window: half a shutter, which comes
off in her hand. She sighs, draws the curtain across it.

                        CORDELIA
              I'm never going to be crowned
              Homecoming Queen, I'm never going to
              graduate high school, I'm never going
              to know if it was real between me and
              Xander or some temporary insanity
              that made me think... I loved him.
                    (starting to cry)
              And now I'll never get to tell him.

                        BUFFY
              Yes you will. We're going to get out
              of here -- then we're going to the
              library where Giles and more weapons
              live -- and we're gonna take the rest
              of these creeps out in time for you
              to congratulate me on my sweeping
              victory as Homecoming Queen.

                                                       CONTINUED

43   CONTINUED:43

                   CORDELIA
I know what you're up to, you think
if you can get me mad enough I won't
be so scared -- and hey, it's
working, where's a damn weapon?!

Cordelia ransacks cupboards and drawers, Buffy moves between
front windows, watches for attack.

                   BUFFY
Do you really love Xander?

                   CORDELIA
Well, he just... grows on you, like
a Chia Pet.

Cordelia joins Buffy at the window, old <u>wooden</u>-handled
spatula in hand.

                   BUFFY
          (re: spatula)
That's it?

                   CORDELIA
Just this and a telephone.

                   BUFFY
Telephone? You didn't think a
telephone would be helpful?

                   CORDELIA
          (re: spatula)
This is better for...
          (mimes hitting, then:)
...oh.

44   EXT. WOODS - NIGHT44

Frederick and Hans move silently through the trees.

45   INT. OLD MAN'S MANSION - NIGHT45

Trick, munching popcorn, strolls up.

                   MR. TRICKS
Popcorn? Not bad for microwave.

                                 CONTINUED

45 CONTINUED: 45

                    OLD MAN
          You're about to see why Daniel Boone
          and that idiot demon are creatures of
          the past, and why I am the future.

                    MR. TRICK
          I love the future. It's just like the
          past, only shiny.

                    OLD MAN
               (re: computer)
          I'm picking up a signal… radio… ?
          They've got a phone!

46 INT. CABIN - NIGHT   46

Buffy, gun in one hand, phone in the other —

                    BUFFY
               (into phone)
          If you get this message, Giles, get
          help, get out here… hello?
               (clicks receiver)

                    CORDELIA
          What happened?

                    BUFFY
          It just went dead.

She drops phone, looks out into the dark night.

47 EXT. ANOTHER PART OF THE WOODS - NIGHT   47

We follow Kulak's blade up to his wounded shoulder. As the
blade moves toward the wound, we MOVE UP to his face which
contorts in pain as he digs (off screen) into the wound.

THE BLADE - drops a spent bullet on the ground.

KULAK'S HAND scoops up mud for a poultice, plasters it to his
Shoulder, then he gets to his feet, starts to walk. He passes:

FRAWLEY - still writhing in agony, his leg in the trap.

                    KULAK
          Want me to cut that leg off for you?

                                             CONTINUED

47   CONTINUED:47

                         FRAWLEY
                      (clenched teeth)
                 No thanks.

Kulak, blade in each hand, moves on.

48   INT. LIBRARY - NIGHT48

Giles pours a cup of tea, notices the BLINKING LIGHT on his
message machine. Hits PLAY.

                         MACHINE VOICE (V.O.)
                 You have one message...

                         BUFFY'S VOICE
                 Giles, it's me. And Cordelia. We're
                 in a cabin in Miller's Woods, we got
                 big trouble...

49   EXT. WOODS - CABIN - NIGHT49

The cabin, nestled in the woods. Frederick and Hans approach
with grenade launcher, stand. PUSHING IN in on the earwig in
Frederick's ear --

50   INT. OLD MAN'S MANSION - NIGHT - THE OLD MAN50

At his computer. Coordinates of the woods on his monitor. And
two red dots. The old man wears a headset.

                         OLD MAN
                      (into headset)
                 I have them both in range.

INSERT - COMPUTER

The grid enlarges, the red dots grow and center, a target
scope zeroes in on them --

                         OLD MAN (O.S.)
                 Northeast Grid A as in apple dash E
                 as in Edward...

51   EXT. WOODS - CABIN - NIGHT51

Hans taps the Coordinates into a key pad on the side of the
grenade launcher as Frederick readies a rocket grenade for
loading.

                    OLD MAN (O.S.)
          ...fourteen point eight degrees by...
          seventy-two point three...

52   INT. CABIN - NIGHT52

Buffy's at the window; Cor clings to her spatula.

                    CORDELIA
          Why is it... every time I go
          somewhere with you, it always ends in
          violence and terror?

                    BUFFY
          Welcome to my life.

                    CORDELIA
          I don't want to be in your life, I
          want to be in mine.

                    BUFFY
          Please feel free to walk out that
          door and live it at any time.

                    CORDELIA
          All I wanted was to be Homecoming
          Queen.

                    BUFFY
          Well that's all I wanted, too,
          Cordelia, I spent a year's allowance
          on this dress...

                    CORDELIA
          I don't get why you even care about
          Homecoming when you're doing stuff
          like this.

                    BUFFY
          Because this is all I do. This is
          what my life is, fighting monsters no
          one even knows about while everyone
          else gets to...
                    (more)

                                              CONTINUED

52   CONTINUED:52

                          BUFFY (cont'd)
              I thought, Homecoming Queen, I could
              open a yearbook someday and say "I
              was there, I went to high school and
              had friends and for just one minute,
              I got to live in the world." And
              there'd be proof. Proof that I was
              chosen for something other than this.
                        (holds up gun)
              ...besides
                        (pumps shell in gun)
              ...I look cute in a tiara.

Cordelia listens.

                          CORDELIA
              Do you hear --

Kulak, screaming bloody murder, dives through the window,
blade in each hand. He knocks Buffy down, the gun goes flying.

53   INT. OLD MAN'S MANSION - NIGHT53

Trick flings popcorn into the air, catching it in his mouth.

                          OLD MAN (INTO HEAD SET)
              Prepare to launch...

54   EXT. WOODS - NIGHT54

Frederick drops the grenade into the launcher.

55   INT. CABIN - NIGHT55

Buffy and Kulak fight. Cordelia tries hitting him on his
spiny head with the spatula. Doesn't do a damn thing, but you
gotta admire her pluck.

                          BUFFY
                        (between punches)
              Cor.. the gun!

Cordy grabs the gun, tries to figure out how to work it as
Buffy takes a slice to the arm. Cor finally gets a shot
off -- blowing a chunk of wood behind Buffy's head away.

                                                      CONTINUED

55   CONTINUED:55

                    BUFFY (cont'd)
          Cor...the spatula!

Kulak nearly takes Buffy's head off as she ducks a blade.
Buffy roundhouse kicks Kulak in the face.

                    CORDELIA
          Buffy!

Cordelia hurls her the gun. She levels it at Kulak -- he
freezes -- she pulls the trigger. Nothing. She works the
action. Fires again. It's empty. Kulak smiles, comes for her.

A56   INT. OLD MAN'S MANSION - NIGHTA56   *

                    OLD MAN   *
          Launch.   *

56   EXT. WOODS - NIGHT56

Frederick fires the grenade launcher!

57   INT. CABIN - NIGHT57

Buffy ducks a blade as the GRENADE blasts through the flimsy
wall, lands on the floor between Buffy and Kulak. They both
look down, then they both turn towards opposite walls.

POSSIBLE SLOW MO - Buffy grabs Cordelia and they crash out the
(unshuttered but curtained) window.

Kulak drives for the opposite (<u>shuttered</u> but curtained window)
and -- REGULAR SPEED -- bounces off the closed shutters.
Kulak looks down at the grenade. Ba' bye.

58   EXT. CABIN - NIGHT58

Blows to smithereens (as Buffy and Cor run towards us.)

ANGLE - BUFFY AND CORDELIA - look up from the ground.

                    BUFFY
          We gotta get to the library.

HER POV: THE TWINS - far away through the smoke, seeing Buffy.

                                                    CONTINUED

                          BUFFY (cont'd)
              ...now.

They scramble to their feet, run.

59   INT. LIBRARY - NIGHT59

PAN - an axe, a sword, and a crossbow as TWO HANDS lock an
arrow onto it. PULLING BACK, we see Candy Gorch, playing with
the crossbow. Lyle moves the arrow away from his heart.

                          GORCH
              Easy darlin', those things'll go
              through ya quicker 'n Grampa Pete's
              chili.

                          CANDY
              I want to do Buffy, my weddin'
              present fer what happened to your
              brother. When's she comin'?

Now we see Giles, lying on the floor, a nasty bruise on his
forehead.

                          GORCH
              He's her Watcher. She'll show as soon as
              she takes out some a our competition.

                          CANDY
              Can I eat 'im?

                          GORCH
              Course you can, sugar. I'm hoping to
              get a little information out of him
              first.
                   (kicks Giles)
              Wish you hadn't clocked him so good.

                          CANDY
              Hell, I hit you harder 'n that.

                          GORCH
              But I'm your husband and I like it.

                          CANDY
                   (seductively)
              Do you?

                                           CONTINUED

                          GORCH   *

                     Gotta have that sugar.

 And they neck. Off Giles,

BLACK OUT.

                    END OF ACT THREE

ACT FOUR

60   INT   OLD MAN'S MANSION - NIGHT60

On COMPUTER: Two red dots moving left through the grids.

> OLD MAN (INTO HEAD SET)
> They're heading West, back into town.

> MR. TRICK
> They got away?

> OLD MAN
> Temporarily...

A SIREN can be heard in the near distance.

> MR. TRICK
> Give it up for the Slayers, they got
> character.
> (problem)
> What do I do if they survive?
> (solution)
> Re-match next year -- bring on the
> money...
> (re: computer)
> ...go girls, go!

Suddenly the sirens are very loud and we HEAR the sound of
screeching tires outside. Then a KNOCK at the front door.

> MR. TRICK (cont'd)
> I'll take care of it.

Mr. Trick leaves the old man, goes to the front door, opens
it. Four UNIFORMED COPS.

> MR. TRICK (cont'd)
> Good evening, gentlemen. What can I
> do for --

They grab him, hustle him away.

> MR. TRICK (cont'd)
> Excuse me, someone have a warrant
> here?

61   INT. SCHOOL HALL - NIGHT61

Cordy (clinging to her spatula) and Buffy move down the hall.
Dresses torn, faces dirty, <u>hair a mess</u>, looking like refugees.

                BUFFY
      Jungle Bob and spike-head are down
      and out, we lost the Germans twice,
      but they seem to keep finding us --
      we take out them and the Gorches, we
      can still make Homecoming.

                CORDELIA
      Those animals, hunting us down like
      poor defenseless... well, animals, I
      guess.

As they enter:

62   INT. LIBRARY - NIGHT62

                BUFFY
      Now we just need --

Candy Gorch kicks Buffy, catching her way off guard. Buffy
slams into a wall. Candy kicks and punches her a couple of
more times -- Buffy's going down -- Cordelia sees Lyle Gorch
coming for her.

                CORDELIA
      Buffy!

Cordy hurls the spatula to Buffy -- as Candy picks up the
coat rack -- Buffy stakes Candy who WALLOPS HER in the head
with the coat rack sending her down and out -- and then turns
to dust.

Candy's pink barrette falls to the floor.

GORCH - About to attack Cordelia, cries out:

                GORCH
      Candy!

He kneels, fishes her barrette out of the dust in grief-
stricken disbelief.

                GORCH (cont'd)
      First ma' brother Tector, now ma'
      wife...

                                    CONTINUED

CORDELIA -- Looks from unconscious Buffy to unconscious
Giles. Not a good sitch. Gorch heads for Buffy.

> GORCH (cont'd)
> I'll kill ya' fer this, Slayer...

GILES' EYES flutter open. Woozy, he witnesses CORDELIA as she
steps in front of Gorch.

> GORCH (cont'd)
> ...you too, you're dead meat, ya'
> hear?!

> CORDELIA
>   (incredibly cool)
> I hear you, you red-neck moron. You
> got a little dress goes with that hat?

PUSH IN ON GORCH - turning read with fury.

> GORCH
> I'm gonna --

> CORDELIA
> I know, rip out my innards, play with
> my eyeballs, boil my brain and eat it
> for brunch -- now listen up, needle-
> brain, Buffy and I have taken out
> four of your cronies, including your
> girlfriend --

> GORCH
> WIFE!

> CORDELIA
> -- whatever, point is, I haven't even
> worked up a sweat. See in the end
> Buffy's good, but she's just the
> runner-up. I'm the Queen. If I get
> mad, what do you think I'm gonna do
> to you?

Gorch looks from Cordy to Buffy and the dust pile on the
floor. Cordy has psyched him out.

> GORCH
> Later!

He runs out. Giles manages to get to his feet. Moves up
behind her.

                                                      CONTINUED

62   CONTINUED: (2)62

                    GILES
          That was...

She spins around, freaked, nearly hits him in the face.

                    CORDELIA
          Bah!

63   INT. MAYOR'S OFFICE - NIGHT63

Mr. Trick is 'helped' inside by the cops, who shut the door,   *
leaving Trick alone with the mayor.   *

                    MAYOR
          Hello. It's nice to meet you.   *

                    MR. TRICK
                 (non-plussed)   *
          Yeah, hi, what a pleasure. Where am   *
          I?   *

                    MAYOR
          In my office. I'm Richard Wilkins,   *
          I'm the Mayor of Sunnydale. And   *
          you're Mr. Trick. Please sit down.   *

Trick does, as the mayor sits behind his desk.   *

                    MAYOR (cont'd)
          That's an exciting suit.   *

                    MR. TRICK
          Clothes make the man.   *

                    MAYOR
          As I understand it, you're not a man   *
          exactly. Mr. Trick, I've been mayor   *
          for quite some time. I like things   *
          to run smoothly. You see, this is a   *
          very important year for me.   *

                    MR. TRICK
          Election year?   *

                    MAYOR
                 (smiling)   *
          Something like that.   *

                                         CONTINUED

63   CONTINUED:63

                    MR. TRICK
          If this is the part where you tell me   *
          I don't fit in your quiet little   *
          neighborhood you can skip it 'cause   *
          that all got old **before** I was a   *
          vampire, you know what I'm saying?   *

                    MAYOR
          Do you have children?   *

                    MR. TRICK
          None living. I think I got some   *
          descendants in Gainsburg or somewhere.   *

                    MAYOR
          Children are the heart of a   *
          community. They have to be looked   *
          after. Controlled. The more   *
          rebellious element needs to be dealt   *
          with.   *

                    MR. TRICK
          I see...   *

                    MAYOR
          The children are our future. We need   *
          them. **I** need them.   *

                    MR. TRICK
          Well, if the 'rebellious element'   *
          means who I think it does, that   *
          problem may take care of itself this   *
          very night.   *

                    MAYOR
          So I've heard. Very enterprising
          idea of yours, SlayerFest. That's   *
          the kind of initiative I need on my   *
          team.   *

                    MR. TRICK
          And what if I don't want to be part   *
          of the team?   *

                    MAYOR
          Oh no, that won't be an issue. You   *
          and I are going to get along very   *
          well.   *

                                              CONTINUED

63   CONTINUED: (2)63

                        He reaches into his desk, offers: *

                    MAYOR (cont'd)   *
        Moist towelette?

64   INT. LIBRARY - NIGHT64

Buffy holds an ice pack to her head. Cordy sits, still
looking a little woozy.

                    GILES
               (to Buffy)
          You should have seen Cordelia.

                    BUFFY
               (to Cordy)
          Teach 'em to mistake you for a slayer.

                    GILES
          I feel somewhat to blame for that, I
          did give your friends tacit approval
          to pull the switch in the limousine...

                    BUFFY
          It wasn't all bad, Cor and I spent
          some quality death time.

                    CORDELIA
          And we got these free corsages.

                    GILES
          I don't recall them saying anything
          about corsages...

                    BUFFY
          No?

Buffy takes off her corsage, studies it.

                    BUFFY (cont'd)
          ...Jungle Bob said the Germans were
          hooked into a computer system...

INSERT - CORSAGE IN BUFFY'S HANDS - SHE TURNS IT

Upside down, peels back a petal. We see a small microship.

                    BUFFY (O.S.)
          ...and they're hooked into us.

Suddenly they hear an exterior door SLAM O.S.

                    CORDELIA
          Oh God! Get rid of that thing.

                                              CONTINUED

64   CONTINUED:64

                    BUFFY
          Give me yours.
                    (thinks)
          I need some wet toilet paper.

                    CORDELIA
          Oh yeah, that'll help.

65   INT. SCHOOL HALL - NIGHT65

Frederick and Hans lower their night vision goggles, raise
their AR-15 semi-automatic rifles with laser sights, move out.   *

NIGHT VISION GOGGLE POV

The empty hall, eerie in the green night vision light, blurry
shapes of things.

66   INT. OLD MAN'S MANSION - NIGHT66

The Old Man at his computer, speaks into his headset.

                    OLD MAN
                    (excited)
          They're fifty feet away!

ON HIS COMPUTER SCREEN - two red dots, next to each other,
growing larger as:

67   INT. SCHOOL HALL - NIGHT67

Buffy bursts out of the library, runs across their path. They
fire! They miss. Frederick motions to Hans -- Hans nods,
heads off after Buffy, Frederick holds his ground in the hall
as:

                    OLD MAN (O.S.)
          I have them, axis six degrees by
          thirty-three...

Frederick turns his gun towards the door to the classroom.

68   INT. SCHOOL HALL - BACK DOOR TO CLASSROOM - NIGHT68

Hans rounds the corner, just sees Buffy entering the class
room. He follows.

                                                  CONTINUED

69   INT. CLASSROOM - NIGHT69

Dark, scary. Hans enters, looks around. Buffy rears up. IN
HER HAND we see the two corsages, wrapped in a bunch of wet
tissue. She flings them like a ball across the room -- they
splat and stick on Han's back. He spins around as --

70   INT. OLD MAN'S MANSION - NIGHT70

ON HIS COMPUTER SCREEN - red dots, large, right next to each
other.

                         OLD MAN
              Both targets, axis seven degrees...

71   INT. SCHOOL HALL - NIGHT71

Frederick aims his gun at the door.

                         OLD MAN (O.S.)
              ...by thirty-five. Fire! Fire!

72   INT. SCHOOL HALL - NIGHT72

Frederick fires! Blasting right through the wall -- hitting: *

73   INT. CLASSROOM - NIGHT73

Hans, who spins and instinctively returns fire.

74   INT. SCHOOL HALL - NIGHT74

Frederick hits the floor, dead.

75   INT. CLASSROOM - NIGHT75

Hans hits the floor, dead.

76   INT. OLD MAN'S MANSION - NIGHT76

He watches, breathless, as the two red dots on his screen go
out. The old bastard can't believe his eyes:

                         OLD MAN
              I won!

                                                         CONTINUED

A lot of excitement in the room, heads turn to watch: *

ON STAGE - Devon, envelope in hand, taps the mic, it feeds   *
back terribly.

                    DEVON
               Okay, guys, it's the moment we've all
               been waiting for...

Willow, Xander, Oz in the crowd, concerned.

                    WILLOW
               They're gonna announce the Queen,
               where are they? What's taking them
               so long?

                    OZ
                    (sees something O.S.)
               I'm gonna go with mud wrestling...

They follow his gaze to: Buffy, Cordelia and Giles arriving.
Buffy and Cor still with the torn dresses, the messed up make-
up and hair. Faith joins Willow, Xander and Oz as Buffy, Cor
and Giles move up.

                    XANDER
               Oh God, what'd you do to each other?

                    BUFFY
               Long story.

                    CORDELIA
               Got hunted.

                    BUFFY
               Apparently not that long.

                    BUFFY (cont'd)
               I'll tell you, though, you don't ever
               want to cross Cordy.

                    XANDER
               Heh, heh -- no.

DEVON ON STAGE

                    DEVON
               In this envelope I hold the name of
               this year's Homecoming Queen.

                                                        CONTINUED

Shows audience envelope. They clap and cheer. Some boo and jeer.

PUSH IN ON BUFFY AND COR

Two war-hardened veterans.

> CORDELIA
> You know after all we've been through
> tonight, this whole who-gets-to-be-
> Queen-capade seems pretty...

> BUFFY
> ...damn important.

> CORDELIA
> Oh yeah.

Devon tears the envelope.

> DEVON
> And the winner is... Hey, I believe
> this is a first for Sunnydale High...
> we have a tie!

Cordelia, and Buffy look at each other and share a weary, warm smile.

> DEVON (cont'd)
> Holly Charleston and Michelle Blake!

Michelle and Holly, fighting tears, shove their way past Buffy and Cor, heading for the stage and glory.

CORONATION MUSIC, confetti and balloons; Devon hold the crown over both their heads. Crowd cheers.

BUFFY AND CORDELIA - Trade a look. After a moment, they head out the door together.

> MICHELLE
> I'm just so honored, I can't believe   *
> it! I mean, that you would have   *
> chosen me -- us -- out of all the   *
> girls in school...

CONTINUED

                    MICHELLE (cont'd)   *
          it's just so... wonderful!
BLACK OUT.

                    MICHELLE (O.S.)
          I have so many people to thank, I
          don't know where to begin!

                    END OF SHOW

BUFFY THE VAMPIRE SLAYER

"Band Candy"

Written By

Jane Espenson

Directed By

Michael Lange

SHOOTING DRAFT

September 14, 1998   (WHITE)
September 16, 1998   (BLUE)

BUFFY THE VAMPIRE SLAYER

"Band Candy

CAST LIST

```
BUFFY SUMMERS........................Sarah Michelle Gellar
XANDER HARRIS........................Nicholas Brendon
RUPERT GILES.........................Anthony S. Head
WILLOW ROSENBERG.....................Alyson Hannigan
CORDELIA CHASE.......................Charisma Carpenter
ANGEL................................David Boreanaz
OZ...................................Seth Green

JOYCE................................Kristine Sutherland
PRINCIPAL SNYDER.....................*Armin Shimerman
MR. TRICK............................K. Todd Freeman
THE MAYOR............................*Harry Groener
ETHAN RAYNE..........................Robin Sachs
MS. BARTON...........................*Peg Stewart
POLICEMAN............................
WORKMAN..............................
MAN..................................
```

BUFFY THE VAMPIRE SLAYER

"Band Candy"

SET LIST

INTERIORS

MAYOR'S OFFICE
SUNNYDALE HIGH SCHOOL
HALLWAY
CAFETERIA
LIBRARY
SCIENCE CLASSROOM
BUFFY'S HOUSE
FOYER
KITCHEN
LIVING ROOM
MANSION
GILES' APARTMENT
JOYCE'S CAR
THE BRONZE
SEDAN
BAND CANDY WAREHOUSE
STATION WAGON
HOSPITAL
NURSES' STATION
MATERNITY WARD
HALLWAY
SEWER

EXTERIORS

CEMETERY
CITY HALL
GILES' APARTMENT
JOYCE'S CAR
MANSION GARDEN
STREET
STOREFRONT
WAREHOUSE LOADING DOCK
SUNNYDALE HIGH SCHOOL
QUAD

"Band Candy"

TEASER

1   EXT. CEMETERY - NIGHT   1

BUFFY kneels, elbows resting on a platform-style headstone,
chin propped on her hands. GILE PACES and reads from a
large book. It appears he is making with the vampire lore.

                    GILES
          "...and on that tragic day, an era
          came to its inevitable end." That's
          all there is. Are you ready?

                    BUFFY
          Hit me.

                    GILES
          Which of the following best expresses
          the theme of the passage? A:
          "violence breeds violence." B: "all
          things must end."

Buffy picks up a standardized test answer sheet from the
headstone. Some filled-in bubbles. Some smudgy erasures.

                    GILES (cont'd)
          C --

                    BUFFY
          I'm putting "B." There hasn't been
          a "B" in forever.

                    GILES
          This is the S.A.T.s, Buffy, not
          "connect-the-dots." Please pay
          attention. A low score could
          seriously harm your chances of
          getting into college.

                    BUFFY
          Oh, that takes the pressure right off.

                    GILES
          This isn't supposed to be easy, you
          know. It's a rite of passage.

                                                        CONTINUED

1   CONTINUED: 1

                          BUFFY
             Is it too late to join a tribe where
             they just pierce something, or cut
             something off?

                          GILES
             Buffy, please. Concentrate.

Buffy suddenly jumps up, and RUNS at Giles. He stares at
her, confused.

                          BUFFY
             Roll!

Giles DROPS, ROLLS. Buffy GOES HIGH, sailing through the air
where Giles had just been -- and where a VAMPIRE now menaces.
She catches it with a KICK, and it staggers back. Buffy
dives after it, and using her pencil, SHE STAKES. The
vampire turns to DUST.

ANGLE: GILES

He picks up his book, adjusts his glasses.

                          BUFFY (cont'd)
             Broke my number two pencil. Sorry.
             We'll have to do this again some--

Giles hands her a new pencil.

                          GILES
             C: "all systems tend toward chaos."

Buffy trudges to pick up her answer sheet off the ground.

                          BUFFY
             I just know us and the undead are the
             only people in Sunnydale working at
             this hour.

2   EXT. CITY HALL - NIGHT - TO ESTABLISH   2

Imposing, dark. One set of office lights glow in the night.

                          THE MAYOR (V.O.)
             I appreciate your coming. I realize
             it is early...

3   INT. MAYOR'S OFFICE - NIGHT   3

The mayor is with Mr Trick.

                                                            CONTINUED

3 CONTINUED: 3

                         THE MAYOR
               ... for you... but I think you'll
               agree this matter is urgent. Also
               delicate.

                         MR. TRICK
               Well, I'm a very delicate person.

                         THE MAYOR
               So you feel you can handle this?

                         MR. TRICK
               It's a little out of my element, but
               I can get you what you need. I know
               a beast who knows a guy.

                         THE MAYOR
               Are you sure subcontracting is the
               way to go here?

                         MR. TRICK
               I believe this guy's worked your town
               before. If he lives up to his rep,
               the place'll be in flames.

                         THE MAYOR
               I've made certain deals to get where
               I am today. This demon requires his
               tribute. You see, that's what
               separates me from other politicians,
               Mr. Trick...

He opens his cabinet to reveal a hideous shrine of evil:
blood markings, goats heads, talisman, you name it.

                         THE MAYOR (cont'd)
               ..I keep my campaign promises.

He picks up a jug made of a shrunken head, sniffs it. It's
not what he wants.

                         THE MAYOR (cont'd)
               Now, where did I put the scotch?

BLACK OUT.

                         END OF TEASER

ACT ONE

4 EXT. SCHOOL QUAD - THE NEXT DAY   4

Buffy, Willow and Oz walk in the quad.

                    BUFFY
          And then I was getting chased by an
          improperly filled-in answer bubble
          yelling "none of the above"!

                    WILLOW
          Wow. I hope that wasn't one of your
          prophecy dreams.
                    (then)
          Probably not.

                    OZ
          You know, Willow and I both took it
          last year. We could help you get
          ready. There's this whole trick to
          antonyms but...
                    (looking around,
                     whispering)
          this isn't the place.

                    WILLOW
          Oz is the highest scoring person ever
          to fail to graduate.

                    BUFFY
                    (to Oz)
          Isn't she cute when she's proud?

                    OZ
          She's always cute.

XANDER and CORDELIA join them.

                    WILLOW
          We could work on it tonight.

                    XANDER
          Work on what tonight?

                    CORDELIA
          Oh god, are we killing something
          again?

                    BUFFY
          Only my carefree spirit.

                                                        CONTINUED

4 CONTINUED: 4

                        OZ
              Buffy S.A.T.-prep

                        WILLOW
              Oz is helping. He's the highest
              scoring person--

                        CORDELIA
              We know. We did the impressed thing
              already.

                        XANDER
              I hate they make us take that thing.
              It's totally fascist, and personally,
              I think it discriminates against the
              uninformed.

                        CORDELIA
              Actually, I'm looking forward to it.
              I do well on standardized tests.
                        (off their looks)
              What? I can't have layers?

5 INT. HALLWAY/CAFETERIA - CONTINUOUS - DAY   5

     They enter near the caf, head there.

                        WILLOW
              So, Buff, study, tonight?

                        BUFFY
              Um... yes on the study, no on
              tonight. Putting in Mom-time. She's
              been like, drastic ever since I got
              back. And Giles is even worse.
              Between the two of them I'm
              supervised twenty-four seven. It's
              like living in the Real World house,
              only real.

     They reach the door and run into PRINCIPAL SNYDER, who is
     handing out cardboard boxes. Startled, they each take one.
     Willow looks inside.

                        WILLOW
                        (pleased)
              Chocolate bars. Lot's of 'em!

                        XANDER
              Principal Snyder, thank you! You
              weren't visited by the ghost of
              Christmas past by any chance?

                                                          CONTINUED

5   CONTINUED: 5

                         PRINCIPAL SNYDER
                    It's band candy.

                         BUFFY
                    Let's hear it for the band, huh?
                    Very generous.

                         PRINCIPAL SNYDER
                    You will sell it. To raise money for
                    the marching band. They need new
                    uniforms.

                         XANDER
                    Those tall fuzzy hats ain't cheap,
                    huh?

                         OZ
                    But they go with everything.

                         BUFFY
                    Um, as much as I'm sure we all love
                    the idea of going all Willy Loman...
                    we're not in the band.

                         PRINCIPAL SNYDER
                    And if I had just handed you a
                    trombone, that would be a problem,
                    Summers. It's candy. Sell it.

          Snyder stalks off. They are left looking at their boxes of
          chocolate merchandise.

6   INT. BUFFY'S KITCHEN - AFTER SCHOOL (DAY)   6

          JOYCE and Buffy eat take-out chinese food.   *

                         JOYCE
                    You're not in the band.

                         BUFFY
                    And yet.

                         JOYCE
                    Buffy, what would I do with forty
                    chocolate bars?

                         BUFFY
                    You could give them out at the
                    gallery. Buy something Pre-
                    Columbian, get a free cavity.

                                                            CONTINUED

6   CONTINUED: 6

                         JOYCE
              Twenty.

                         BUFFY
              You're a good mom.

                         JOYCE
              I'm the best.

                         BUFFY
                    (playful)
              Oh, I'm pretty sure the best moms let
              their daughters drive.

                         JOYCE
              And yet.

                         BUFFY
              Come on--

                         JOYCE
              Oh, let's not have this conversation.

                         BUFFY
              I took the class. And I watched all
              the filmstrips with the blood and the
              death and the corpses -- I'm prepped!

                         JOYCE
              Honey, you failed the written test.
              They wouldn't even let you take the
              road test.

                         BUFFY
              That was a year ago. And I don't
              test well. She said, two days before
              the S.A.T.s.

                         JOYCE
              I spend enough time not knowing where
              you are. I don't want to add the
              possibility that you're on the
              highway to Chicago.

                         BUFFY
              I can't believe you. I'm not going
              to take off again. And if I was, I
              could just get on a bus--

                         JOYCE
              Stop. Don't. I just... don't want
              you driving, okay? I want you here.

                                                      CONTINUED

6 CONTINUED: (2)   6

                    BUFFY
          Okay, I'm here. See me being here.

Buffy eats her last bite of pizza.

                    BUFFY (cont'd)
          Gotta go.

Buffy gets up.

                    JOYCE
          What? You're going out?

                    BUFFY
          Giles. Study-slay double feature.
          Could be late.

                    BUFFY
          Again? Honey, don't you think Mr.
          Giles is monopolizing an awful lot of
          your time?

                    BUFFY
          And does he ever say he's sorry?

7 INT. LIBRARY - LATER (NIGHT)   7

Giles is tying a blindfold over Buffy's eyes. He accidently
pulls her hair.

                    BUFFY
          Ow!

                    GILES
          Sorry.

                    BUFFY
          Why do I put up with this?

                    GILES
          Because it is your destiny and
          because I just bought twenty
          "cocorific" candy bars.

Giles puts a ball into Buffy's hands. It's the inflated
rubber kind used to play dodge ball.

                    BUFFY
          Okay, now you're just doing this to
          take funny pictures of me.

                                                         CONTINUED

302

7 CONTINUED: 7

                    GILES
          I'm testing your awareness of an
          opponent's location during a fight in
          total darkness. You're to wait five
          seconds, then throw me the ball.

As Buffy talks, Giles circles around behind her. Buffy
continues to talk to where he was.

                    BUFFY
          You ran out of training ideas about
          a week ago, didn't you? Okay. Five,
          four, three-two-one.

She TURNS AWAY FROM GILES, and throws the ball -- it clearly
will miss Giles by a mile.

                    GILES
          Not so simple, is--

As Giles speaks, the ball RICOCHETS off a wall and HITS GILES
IN THE HEAD.

                    GILES (cont'd)
          Ow. Ah. Well done.

Buffy takes off the blindfold.

                    BUFFY
          Thanks.

Buffy heads for the door.

                    GILES
          Wait, you're not going? We have to
          patrol.

                    BUFFY
          Can't. I told you, Mom's in
          hyperdrive. She wants me home
          tonight.

                    GILES
          Oh. But--

Buffy picks up her box of candy and hands it to Giles.

                    BUFFY
          I know. She's out of control. Enjoy
          the candy!

And she's out. Resigned, Giles takes a candy bar out of the
box and starts to unwrap it.

303

8   INT. MANSION - NIGHT   8

Buffy, holding a grocery bag, lets herself in. She looks
around. No Angel. She heads toward the courtyard.

EXT. MANSION GARDEN - CONTINUOUS - NIGHT

Buffy enters to find Angel shirtless, glistening with
perspiration, and doing Tai Chi. She starts to speak, but
then just watches. Finally, he turns, gracefully, part of
the routine, and sees her.

                    ANGEL
          Buffy.

                    BUFFY
          I didn't know you could do that.

He walks toward her.

                    ANGEL
          I'm doing better...

He stumbles.

                    BUFFY
          Angel!

She grabs him and steadies him. She puts her arms around him
and helps him back into the mansion.

10   INT. MANSION - NIGHT   10

Still with an arm around him, she helps Angel to a chair.
Suddenly they are both aware of the contact. He moves away
from her. Angel looks at everything in the room except her.

                    ANGEL
          It's late. How did you get away?

                    BUFFY
          Easy. Started a fire in the prison
          laundry, rode out in the garbage
          truck.

                    ANGEL
          Oh.

                    BUFFY
          Joking. No garbage. Smell me.

Now he's too close. He looks at her a moment, then:

                                                        CONTINUED

                        ANGEL
              How is... Scott?

                        BUFFY
              Oh, Scott, Boyfriend Scott, actually
              he's not-- He's fine.

Buffy hands him a grocery bag.

                        BUFFY (cont'd)
              I brought more... for you. From the
              butcher's.

He takes the bag, removes a take-out soup container. Through
the lid, the liquid inside is visibly red.

                        ANGEL
              Thank you.

He sets it aside awkwardly. Finally he looks at her, really
meeting her eyes.

                        ANGEL (cont'd)
              You're being careful, right?

                        BUFFY
              With Scott?

                        ANGEL
              The slaying.

                        BUFFY
              Oh, of course. Yeah, sure I am. I'm
              full of carefulness.

                        ANGEL
              I worry about you.

                        BUFFY
              Likewise.

                        ANGEL
              I'm getting stronger.

                        BUFFY
              Yeah. Soon you won't need me.

                        ANGEL
              That'll be better.

                        BUFFY
                   (no it won't)
              Yeah.

                                                    CONTINUED

11   INT. BUFFY'S HOUSE - FOYER - LATER - NIGHT   11

Buffy comes in through the front door to find Joyce standing
in the foyer. Joyce is unwrapping a band candy bar.

                    BUFFY
          Hi. Sorry I'm late, but you know
          Giles. All slay, all the time.

Giles walks around from behind Buffy.

                    GILES
          Hello, Buffy.

                    BUFFY
          Hi. Um... you guys want to watch TV?
          I hear Nightline's very insightful.

                    JOYCE
          You lied to us, Buffy. And you made
          us into your alibis. That's playing
          us against each other and that's not
          fair.

                    GILES
          I called Willow. You lied to her
          about your whereabouts also. We were
          all concerned.

Joyce holds out her candy bar toward Giles, offering. He
breaks off a piece.

                    GILES (cont'd)
                 (to Joyce)
          Thank you.

They both nibble throughout the following.

                    BUFFY
          I'm sorry. It's just, I had to go--

Buffy walks into the --

12   INT. BUFFY'S HOUSE - LIVING ROOM - CONTINUOUS - NIGHT   12

No escape, they both follow her.

                    JOYCE
          Were you at the Bronze? What was
          happening there that was so important?

                    BUFFY
          Oh. Um... Bronze things. Things of
          Bronze.

                                        CONTINUED

                         JOYCE
          You're acting really immature, Buffy.

                         GILES
          I know I'm not your parent, but I do
          have to look after you. Your mom's
          right.

                         BUFFY
          Okay, so I'm acting like a child.
          Maybe that's because you're both
          treating me like a child.

                         JOYCE
          Buffy!

                         BUFFY
          No. Listen. You're both scheduling
          me twenty-four hours a day, and
          between the two of you, that's...
          forty-eight hours, and I just want to
          make some decisions on my own.

                         JOYCE
          The last time you made a decision on
          your own you split.

                         BUFFY
          And I took care of myself just fine.
          I don't need quite this much "active
          parenting," thank you very much.

                         JOYCE
          You can't really be trying to use
          this summer as a reason you should be
          trusted!

                         BUFFY
          Mom, you gotta back off some! I
          don't need to be baby-sat.

                         GILES
          All right, come on. Let's not freak
          out.

                         BUFFY
          Let's not what?

                         GILES
          I think you should go to bed. We're
          all tired.

                                                      CONTINUED

12 CONTINUED: (2)   12

Buffy hesitates, considering continuing the engagement. She
senses the futility, and turns on her heel... off to bed.
After she's gone:

                    JOYCE
                (to Giles)
          She drives me crazy. I just want to
          protect her.

                    GILES
          All parents want that.

                    JOYCE
          Yeah, but at least most parents know
          what to protect their children from.

                    GILES
          Yeah, you and I have to be especially
          careful.

Giles pulls another band candy bar out of his jacket pocket.
He offers a piece to Joyce. They enjoy it silently.

CLOSE ON: A BAND CANDY BAR

Sitting with many others of its kind in a box.

WIDEN TO SHOW

13 INT. WAREHOUSE - NIGHT   13

A MAN, in factory coveralls, who seals the filled box and
reaches for the next box. He glances around, reaches in,
removes a bar. He peels back the wrapper, and is ready to
chomp when...

A HAND

LOCKS AROUND HIS WRIST... WE FOLLOW THE ARM UP TO REVEAL:
ETHAN RAYNE.

                    ETHAN
          Trust me. You don't want to eat that.

     BLACK OUT.

                    END OF ACT ONE

ACT TWO

INT. SCIENCE CLASSROOM - THE NEXT DAY   14

14

A science classroom, with two-person tables. The STUDENTS
wait for the teacher. Buffy and Cordelia share a table.
Xander and Willow have the table behind them.

                    CORDELIA
          I hear there's this secret rule if
          a teacher is over ten minutes late,
          everyone can leave.

                    BUFFY
          It's Giles' turn to lead study hall.
          He'll be here. He's allergic to late.

                    CORDELIA
          The man is wrapped a little tight.
          I had this philosophy book out from
          the library for like a year and he
          made me pay the fine even though it
          was huge. I eventually had to return
          it, which was sad because it was
          perfect for starting conversations
          with college boys. Of course, that
          was B.X.

                    BUFFY
          B.X? Oh, Before Xander. Clever.

ANGLE: THE TABLE BEHIND THEM

Xander, eating a band candy bar, sits next to Willow.

                    XANDER
          I like chocolate. There's no bad
          here.

                    WILLOW
          You still have some left? I went to
          like four houses and they were gone.
          It was like trick-or-treating in
          reverse.

                    XANDER
          I know, they're selling like hot
          cakes. Which is ironic, 'cause the
          hot cakes really aren't moving.

ANGLE: THEIR KNEES

                                                    CONTINUED

14 CONTINUED: 14

Under the table. They both slowly move their legs together
until their knees are touching.

                    WILLOW
                  (distracted)
          We're raising a lot of money for the
          band.

                    XANDER
                  (also distracted)
          Yeah. They're great. They march.

                    WILLOW
                  (not listening to
                   herself)
          Like an army. With music instead of
          bullets and usually no one dies.

Xander inches his foot over to nudge Willow's. She crosses
her foot over his... twining ankles. Ankle sex.

                    CORDELIA (cont'd)
          I can't believe this!

Willow and Xander jump apart, SLAMMING their knees into the
table legs. Xander whimpers. Willow bites her lip.

                    CORDELIA (cont'd)
          Where is Giles already? I'm bored
          and he's not here to give me credit
          for it.

ANGLE: PRINCIPAL SNYDER

And an older teacher, MS. BARTON, are engaged in a whispered
conversation in the classroom doorway. Snyder is eating a
band candy bar.

                    PRINCIPAL SNYDER
          Look, the big pinhead librarian
          didn't show up and I don't want to do
          it. You do it.

                    MS. BARTON
          All right. Fine. I'll do it.

She moves to the front of the room, and Snyder heads out.

                    PRINCIPAL SNYDER
                  (to himself)
          Everyone expects me to do everything
          around here 'cause I'm the principal
          and it's not fair...

                                              CONTINUED

14 CONTINUED: (2)   14

Snyder exits. The students continue to chatter.

                    MS. BARTON
                 (very tough)
            Hey, hey!

The students look up, startled.

                    MS. BARTON (cont'd)
            Look, we're all stuck here, okay? So
            let's just sit here quietly...
                 (lowering her voice)
            And pretend to read or something
            until we're sure Commandant Snyder is
            gone, and then we're all out of here.

The students look at each other, happy and surprised.

                    XANDER
            Anyone else want to marry Ms. Barton?

                    CORDELIA
            Get in line.

Ms. Barton sets down her purse.

ANGLE: THE PURSE

No one notices the BAND CANDY BAR sticking out of it.

                    WILLOW
            I guess Giles isn't coming.

                    BUFFY
                 (concerned)
            I guess not.

15   EXT. GILES' PLACE - LATER THAT AFTERNOON (DAY)15

Buffy is at Giles' door. It's slightly ajar. Immediately on
the alert, she pushes her way in silently--

16   INT. GILES' PLACE - CONTINUOUS - DAY16

-- and enters, crouching and tense, to find Giles going
through a file cabinet and Joyce on the couch.

                    GILES
            Buffy!

                                              CONTINUED

16 CONTINUED: 16

                          JOYCE
                Oh!

Buffy relaxes.

                          BUFFY
                Sorry. I was worried, Giles. You
                were a big not-there in study hall
                and after your lecture on me not
                ducking out and what is my mother
                doing here?

                          GILES
                We had an opportunity for a, you
                might say, a summit meeting. It took
                priority over study hall. I called
                in.

                          BUFFY
                Oh.

                          JOYCE
                We decided you made a good point
                earlier, honey.

                          BUFFY
                I did. Yes. And that was...?

                          JOYCE
                About us over-scheduling you.

                          GILES
                Pulling you in two directions, as it
                were... your home life and your
                duties as a slayer.

                          BUFFY
                Oh. That was a good point.

                          JOYCE
                We're working out a coordinated
                schedule for you.

                          GILES
                It will be tight, but I think we can
                fit in all your responsibilities.

                          BUFFY
                     (less enthused)
                Sounds nice 'n' structured.

Joyce comes over to Buffy.

                                                        CONTINUED

                            312

16   CONTINUED: (2)   16

                         JOYCE
               We've got more work to do here,
               honey. Why don't you give us a
               little more time? Take the car. Mr.
               Giles can drive me home.

Sure enough, Joyce is holding out CAR KEYS.

                         BUFFY
               What? Excuse me, I meant: what?

                         JOYCE
               Keys. Take them.

                         BUFFY
               Hey, you don't have to tell me twice.
               Well, you did. But... bye.

Buffy grabs the keys and heads for the door fast, before
Joyce can change her mind.

                         JOYCE
               Bye, honey. Be careful.

Buffy waves and EXITS. Joyce turns to Giles.

                         JOYCE (cont'd)
               You think she noticed anything?

                         GILES
               No way.

Joyce bounces on her knees on the couch and reaches behind it
for a Kalua bottle. Giles lights a cigarette.

17   INT. JOYCE'S CAR - EARLY EVENING (NIGHT)   17

Buffy drives happily. Willow's in the passenger seat.

                         WILLOW
               Tell me again how it happened.

                         BUFFY
               I told her I wanted to be treated
               more like a grown-up, and voila!
               Driviness.

18   EXT. JOYCE'S CAR - CONTINUOUS - NIGHT1   8

Buffy takes a curve with enthusiasm and speed.

                                                    CONTINUED

19   INT. JOYCE'S CAR - CONTINUOUS - NIGHT   19

Willow braces herself with both hands.

                         WILLOW
               Ooh.

                         BUFFY
               Also, I think Mom might've wanted me,
               you know, otherwhere. Giles and her
               are planning my future and I guess
               it's easier to live my life if I'm
               not actually there.

                         WILLOW
               You know you've got the parking brake
               on?

                         BUFFY
               Uh-huh.

Buffy releases it.

                         WILLOW
               Are you sure about the Bronze? The
               S.A.T.s are tomorrow.

                         BUFFY
               I can study at the Bronze. A little
               dancing, a little cross-multiplying.
               Hey, you know what we need?

Buffy starts hitting radio buttons: rock, rap, country...

                         WILLOW
                      (terrified)
               Eyes on the road! Eyes on the road!

20   EXT. JOYCE'S CAR - NIGHT   20

The CAR RADIO BLARES as they WEAVE down the street. The
music changes one more time...

21   INT. GILES' PLACE - LATER (NIGHT)   21

CREAM PLAYS. Giles' button-down is open, revealing a white   *
t-shirt-style undershirt. He lies on his back by his record
player amid scattered albums. Joyce is mixing a Kahlua and
Pepsi. Cigarettes smoulder in an ashtray on the floor.

                         JOYCE
               You've got good albums.

                                                        CONTINUED

21   CONTINUED: 21

                         GILES
                Yeah, they're all right.

Giles' accent is more working class than we're used to.

                         JOYCE
                Do you like Seals and Croft?
                     (off his look)
                Me neither.

He lights another cig, hands it to her. She smokes it
awkwardly... a new smoker.

                         JOYCE (cont'd)
                How come they call you Ripper?

                         GILES
                Wouldn't **you** like to know.

He stops, listening.

                         GILES (cont'd)
                Hey, listen to this bit. It rocks.

Giles turns the volume up.

                         JOYCE
                It's good.

                         GILES
                Man. I gotta get a band together.

                         JOYCE
                So, you wanna watch TV, Ripper? I
                know how to order pay-per-view.

                         GILES
                Let's go out. Have some fun. Tear
                things up.

                         JOYCE
                Okay. We could go to the Bronze.

                         GILES
                Not bloody likely. That place is
                dead.

22   INT. THE BRONZE - EVENING (NIGHT)   22

The joint is jumping: packed and very loud. Buffy enters.
Willow follows, still shaky from the ride.

                                                        CONTINUED

22   CONTINUED: 22

DINGOES ATE MY BABIES PLAYS and looks out at an unusually old
audience. Oz waves at Willow and gives a little shrug.
Everywhere they look, the patrons are ADULTS: at the bar, on
the dance floor. The teenagers in the place are reacting
pretty much the same as Buffy and Willow -- staring in
confusion.

                         BUFFY
              Whoa. Let's do the time warp again.

                         WILLOW
              Maybe there's some kind of reunion in
              town or a Billy Joel tour or
              something.

A WOMAN pushes past them. Buffy recognizes her:

                         BUFFY
              Ms. Barton?

It is her. She blinks owlishly at Buffy, trying to focus.

                         MS. BARTON
              Buffy? Whoa.

                         WILLOW
              You okay, Ms. Barton?

                         MS. BARTON
              I'm cool, Willow. Willow. That's a
              tree. You're a tree. Do they have
              nachos here, little tree?

Ms. Barton starts to laugh, a little out of control.

                         BUFFY
              I think maybe you need some fresh air.

                         MS. BARTON
              Okay.

She amiably drifts off toward the door. Buffy and Willow
watch her go.

                         WILLOW
              Okay, this is not normal.
                   (off Buffy's look)
              Maybe that goes without saying.

                         GUY'S VOICE (O.S.)
              Hey, gang!

                                                           CONTINUED

22 CONTINUED: (2)   22

Buffy and Willow turn, probably expecting to see Xander.
Instead:

                    PRINCIPAL SNYDER
                      (continuing)
              This place is fun city, huh?

                    BUFFY
              Principal Snyder?

                    PRINCIPAL SNYDER
              Call me Snyder. Just a last name.
              Like Barbarino. Whoo! I'm stoked!
              Did you see Ms. Barton? I think   *
              she's wasted. I'm gonna put that on
              her performance review because
              I'm the principal.

The MUSIC FALTERS for a second. They turn and look.

ANGLE: THE STAGE

A SHIRTLESS PUDGY ADULT DIVES OFF THE STAGE, hooting and
hollering. He is almost caught, but the out-of-shape men
beneath him aren't up to it. He ends up on the floor, and
gets to his feet slowly. A lot of the men are red-faced,
sweaty, panting.

ANGLE: WILLOW AND BUFFY

                    WILLOW
              I don't like this. They could have
              heart attacks.

                    BUFFY
              Maybe there's a doctor here.

                    WILLOW
              Actually, that is my doctor. He's
              usually less... topless.

                    PRINCIPAL SNYDER
              I got a commendation. For being
              principal. From the mayor. He shook
              my hand twice.

A clique of THREE OR FOUR MIDDLE-AGED WOMEN scurry past,
laughing and shrieking.

                    PRINCIPAL SNYDER (cont'd)
              Ooh. There's some foxy ladies here
              tonight!

                                                    CONTINUED

22   CONTINUED: (3)   22

                        WILLOW
                      (to Buffy)
              Buffy, what's happening?

                        BUFFY
              I don't know, but it's happening to
              a whole lotta grownups.

                        WILLOW
              They're acting like a bunch of...

                        BUFFY
              They're acting like a bunch of us.

         A beat, as the two girls look worriedly around them.

                        WILLOW
              I don't act like this...

23   INT. BAND CANDY WAREHOUSE - NIGHT   23

         The production line again. Mr. Trick stands with Ethan,
         watching the packing, the sealing, the shipping of the candy.

                        MR. TRICK
              Demand's high.

                        ETHAN
              I thought it might be.

                        MR. TRICK
              That's why I love this country. You
              make a good product, and the people
              will come to you. Of course, a lot
              of them are gonna die, but, well,
              that's the other reason I love this country.

         ANGLE: WORKERS

         A WORKMAN (not the same guy from before) speaks softly to the
         man next to him. Mr. Trick approaches.

                        MR. TRICK (cont'd)
              Hey. No sampling the product.

                        WORKMAN
                      (terrified)
              I didn't--

         Mr. Trick TAKES THE MAN BY THE NECK AND BREAKS IT SWIFTLY.
         THE MAN SLUMPS, DEAD, TO THE FLOOR. The other workers stare,

                                                        CONTINUED

23   CONTINUED: 23

horrified. Mr. Trick turns back to Ethan.

                    ETHAN
                (shaken)
          Okay. Um... how did you know he'd
          taken some?

                    MR TRICK
          I don't. But I know no one else will.   *
                (looks at his watch)   *
          We're getting close. Keep it   *
          flowing. Time for me to get the   *
          goods.
                                                          *

He heads out.

24   INT. THE BRONZE - NIGHT   24

Things are even wilder than they were a minute ago. The band
has given up entirely. Oz stands with Buffy and Willow.

                    BUFFY
          Something's changing them.

                    WILLOW
          A spell?

                    OZ
          They're teenagers. Sobering mirror
          to look into, huh?

                    PRINCIPAL SNYDER
                (to Oz)
          You've got great hair.

THE STAGE

A group of OLD GUYS (shirtless doctor and his buddies) cling
to microphones and belt out LOUIE LOUIE. On the floor
several adult couples are dirty dancing. One couple has
given up on the dancing and stands on the dance floor, making
out.

                    WILLOW
          It just gets more upsetting.

                    BUFFY
          No vampire has ever been that scary.

ANGLE: THE BAR

                                                    CONTINUED

24   CONTINUED: 24

Adults are doing that thing where you lie back on the bar and
the bartender mixes the drink right in your mouth. One adult
accidentally jostles another adult and a MINOR SCUFFLE breaks
out.

                    PRINCIPAL SNYDER
              Fight!   Fight!

Buffy and Oz and Willow move away from the scuffle. The
party is heading toward chaos. They have to talk over the
noise.

                    BUFFY
              We've gotta go find out what's going
              on. This has Hellmouth fingerprints
              all over it. Or, mouthprints...

Buffy leads the way toward the door. Oz and Willow follow.
Snyder loses interest in the fight as it dies down. He tags
along.

                    PRINCIPAL SNYDER
              Where are we going?

They ignore him. At the door, Buffy passes an adult eating
a BAND CANDY BAR. WE SEE HER TAKE NOTICE OF THIS. Buffy,
Willow and Oz duck out the door. A second later...

                    PRINCIPAL SNYDER (cont'd)
              You guys aren't trying to ditch me,
              are you?

Snyder scurries out after them.

25   INT. JOYCE'S CAR - NIGHT   25

Buffy, Willow, Oz are in the car, Willow in the front seat
next to Buffy. Buffy closes her door. She hasn't started
the car yet.

                    OZ
              We should go find Giles, right?
              He'll figure out what's going on.

                    BUFFY
              Sure, except for all we know he's
              sweet sixteen again.

Buffy and Willow share a look- realizing what that could mean.

                                                          CONTINUED

25 CONTINUED: 25

                         WILLOW
                        (to Buffy)
            He's with your mom at his place.

Buffy starts the car. And Snyder opens the door and climbs
in next to Oz.

                    PRINCIPAL SNYDER
            Hey, I said "wait up"!

                         OZ
            Um... Snyder...

                         BUFFY
            No time. He's coming with us.

She pulls out. The TIRES SQUEAL.

                    PRINCIPAL SNYDER
            Whoa, Summers, you drive like a spaz.

26 EXT. STREET - NIGHT   26

A sedan sits at a stoplight. Next to the Sedan, a VOLVO
STATION WAGON revs its engine. It has a bumper sticker: "My
child hearts Sunnydale preschool."

27 INT. SEDAN - NIGHT   27

A BUSINESS MAN clutches the wheel, REVS his engine.

25 INT. STATION WAGON - NIGHT   28

A DOMESTICATED FATHER in a cardigan REVS his engine.

28 EXT. STREET - NIGHT   29

The stoplight turns green. Tires SQUEAL as the cars take off.

30 INT. JOYCE'S CAR - NIGHT   30

Buffy slams on the brakes as the two cars pass (off screen if
necessary) in front of her. She and the others watch them
recede in the distance. Snyder hoots, enjoying the
competition.

                                                          CONTINUED

30 CONTINUED: 30

                        PRINCIPAL SNYDER
              This is great! Let's go do doughnuts
              on the football field.

                        WILLOW
                  (convincing herself)
              It'll be okay when we get to Giles.

                        OZ
              Of course. I mean, even if he's
              sixteen, he's still Giles. Probably
              a pretty together guy.

                        WILLOW
              Yeah, well.

                        OZ
              What?

                        BUFFY
              Giles at sixteen. Less "together
              guy," more "bad magic, hates the
              world, ticking time-bomb guy."

                        OZ
              Oh. Well then, I guess your mom is
              in a lot of trouble.

30 EXT. STOREFRONT - NIGHT   31

     Giles and Joyce walk down the street. Giles has his
     cigarette pack rolled up in his t-shirt sleeve. His arm is
     around Joyce's shoulders, a cigarette in his hand. She
     clings to his other hand and chews gum.

                        JOYCE
              It must be exciting, being from
              England.

                        GILES
              It's all right. Hey, you're not cold
              or anything?

                        JOYCE
              Nuh-uh. I feel... special. Like I'm
              just waking up, kind of.

                        GILES
              How's that?

                                                            CONTINUED

34 CONTINUED: 31

                         JOYCE
              You know, like having a kid and
              getting married and everything was a
              dream and now things are back like
              they're supposed to be.

                         GILES
              Yeah.

Joyce stops, looks at a coat in a store window.

                         JOYCE
              That's cool. Kind of Juice Newton.

                         GILES
              You fancy it?

                         JOYCE
              But the store's not open.

Giles hoists a heavy trash can, and THROWS it. It hits the
store window with a CRASH. The window SHATTERS, sending
glass everywhere. Giles ducks through the window frame,
pulls the coat from its mannequin. He steps back out, and
hands the coat to Joyce.

                         GILES
              Here.

                         JOYCE
              Oh, Ripper, wow. That was so brave.

She's putting on her coat, when...

                         POLICEMAN (O.S.)
              Hold it!

ANGLE: A POLICEMAN approaches, GUN DRAWN.

32 INT. JOYCE'S CAR - NIGHT   32

Buffy heads into an intersection.

33 EXT. STREET - NIGHT   33

A speeding car goes right through the red light at the
intersection. It's heading right for Buffy.

34 INT. JOYCE'S CAR - NIGHT   34

                              WILLOW
                    Oh my god! Look out!

Snyder YELPS.

35 EXT. STREET - NIGHT   35

    CRASH -- The speeding car hits the driver's side of Joyce's
    car, which is rocked by the impact -- dented and thrown back.

    No motion is visible inside.

    BLACK OUT.

                        END OF ACT TWO

ACT THREE

36   EXT. STOREFRONT - CONTINUOUS - NIGHT   36

Giles and Joyce face the armed policeman.

                    GILES
          Oh, copper's got a gun. You'll never
          use it.

                    POLICEMAN
          Will so.

ANGLE: A BAND CANDY BAR

It sticks out of the cop's uniform pocket.

                    JOYCE
          Ripper, be careful!

The cop's eyes flick toward Joyce, the quickest of glances.
It's enough. Giles POUNDS him with A SERIES OF BRUTAL
PUNCHES, then grabs the guy's head and WHIPS IT DOWN to
IMPACT WITH GILES' RAISED KNEE. The guy goes down,
unconscious. The GUN is still clutched in the cop's hand.
Giles takes it, tucks it into his waistband.

                    GILES
          Told him he'd never use it.

                    JOYCE
          You are so cool. You're like Burt
          Reynolds.

Joyce sidles closer, looks up into Giles' eyes. Giles grabs
her, hard. She gasps. He goes in for the kiss, their
eyes locked on each other.

She reaches up and takes the gum out of her mouth. He starts
kissing her, and they sink into the hood of the squad car,
slowly going out of frame.

37   EXT. STREET - NIGHT   37

Slowly, Buffy, Willow, Oz and Snyder get out of the car. The
doors on the damaged side of the car SHRIEK in protest when
they open them. Oz gingerly flexes a bruised elbow. Buffy
has a cut on her forehead. They look at the damaged car.

                    WILLOW
          Is anyone else all creeped out and
          trembly?

                                        CONTINUED

37   CONTINUED: 37

Oz puts his arm around Willow protectively.

                    PRINCIPAL SNYDER
               Buffy, your mom's gonna kill you.

Buffy looks around at the street.

                    BUFFY
                  (thoughtful)
               Something's weird.

                    OZ
               Something's not?

A GANG

of aging greasers loiters at the corner. A woman/girl walks
by. They whistle and catcall. She giggles.

                    BUFFY
               No grown ups. No one's protecting
               their houses, people out wandering
               around--

                    WILLOW
                  (getting it)
               Defenseless.

An OLD MAN strolls by. He STRIPS THE CANDY BAR OUT OF
SNYDER'S HAND and takes off running.

                    PRINCIPAL SNYDER
               Hey! Give it!

BACK ON BUFFY

                    BUFFY
               So where are all the vampires?
               Soup's on, but no one's grabbing a
               spoon.

                    OZ
               Something's happening somewhere
               that's else.

                    BUFFY
               I'm guessing something pretty big.

                    PRINCIPAL SNYDER
               That guy took my candy!

It's starting to add up. Buffy goes to Snyder.

                                                    CONTINUED

37   CONTINUED: (2)   37

                         BUFFY
              What's with the candy? A curse?

                         PRINCIPAL SNYDER
                    (scared)
              A curse? I've got a curse?

                         WILLOW
              Oh my god. Using candy for evil.

                         OZ
              My parents ate a ton.

Buffy backs Snyder up against the car. She's in his face.

                         BUFFY
              Who's behind the candy?

                         PRINCIPAL SNYDER
              I don't know. It came to be through
              the school board, and if you knew
              that crowd...

He shudders.

                         BUFFY
              Where is it? Where would you go for
              more? Do you know?

He nods miserably. Buffy turns to Willow and Oz.

                         BUFFY
              You two, get Xander and Cordelia, go
              to the library. Look it up.

                         OZ
              Candy, curses...

                         WILLOW
              Disturbing second childhood. Got it.

                         BUFFY
              Ratboy and I are going to the source.

She pushes Snyder toward the dented car.

38   EXT. WAREHOUSE LOADING DOCK - LATER - NIGHT   38

CLOSE ON: A BOX OF BAND CANDY BARS

A man's hand reaches in, grabs a handful, THROWS THEM to a

                                              CONTINUED

WAITING CROWD of adults.

They jump and dive for the candy.

WIDEN TO REVEAL the scene:

Two MEN in factory coveralls are standing on the warehouse
loading platform, throwing candy to the crowd like rice at a
wedding.

JOYCE'S CAR

As Buffy and Snyder get out of it. Snyder immediately goes
over to get more candy. Buffy walks by a COUPLE IN A CLINCH,
making out. She stops, looks back at them:

                    BUFFY
          Giles? Mom?!

                    GILES
          Go 'way. We're busy.

They keep kissing. Buffy grabs them each by an arm and pulls
them away from the crowd.

                    JOYCE
          Hey!

                    BUFFY
          Mom--
              (notices)
          Where'd you get that coat? Never
          mind, listen to me--

Giles pulls roughly out of Buffy's grasp. He balls up his
fists.

                    BUFFY (cont'd)
          Okay, Giles. Think. You really want
          to fight me? Or you want to let me
          talk to my mother?

Giles backs down, but in the coolest possible way. He
wanders a few steps away and lights a cigarette as if he were
too cool to care. Buffy looks at Joyce searchingly.

                    BUFFY (cont'd)
          Mom, look at me. Do you know who I
          am?

                    JOYCE
          Of course. You're Buffy. They're
          giving away candy. Want some candy?

                                                      CONTINUED

38   CONTINUED: (2)   38

                    BUFFY
          No. And you don't need any more
          either.

                    JOYCE
          I'm fine. I can have more if I want.

                    BUFFY
          You're not fine. Go home.

                    JOYCE
          Screw you. I want candy.

Buffy recoils as if slapped.

                    BUFFY
          Mom!

                    JOYCE
          Hey look, you want to slay stuff and
          I'm not allowed to do anything about
          it?? Well, this is what I want to do.
          So get off my back.

                    BUFFY
               (genuinely upset)
          Mom. Please.

                    GILES
          For god's sake, let your mum have the
          bleedin' candy. Come on, Joyce.

Giles and Joyce start to walk away. Buffy tries one last
shot.

                    BUFFY
          Wait. Look for one sec. Your car.
          The dent the size of New Brunswick?
          I did that.

Joyce looks toward the car.

                    JOYCE
          Oh my god. What was I thinking when
          I bought the geek machine?

Giles laughs. Buffy takes the cigarette from his mouth, and
throws it on the ground.

                    BUFFY
          Take her home.

                                                   CONTINUED

38   CONTINUED: (3)   38

                         GILES
              Hey. I'm the watcher. You have to
              do what I say. So bugger off.

Giles and Joyce defiantly head back to where the candy is
being handed out. Buffy hesitates, then, her jaw set, she
marches behind them...

She passes them... and without slowing down, she marches to
the base of the loading platform and looks up at the two men
handing out the candy. She reaches up, grabs one by the
ankle, and PULLS HIS FOOT OUT FROM UNDER HIM. He falls over
the edge, at Buffy's feet. He CRUMPLES and Buffy mounts the
steps to the platform. Buffy is now facing the other man.

                         MAN
              Hey, what--

He drops his box of candy. She grabs him by the back of his
coveralls, and tosses him over the edge of the loading
platform, where he lands on the first guy, who CRUMPLES
AGAIN. She throws the boxes of candy down on them, hard.
Adults dive after the candy windfall.

Buffy spots Joyce in the crowd. Buffy leans over, grabs
Joyce's arm, HAULS her up the steps.

                         JOYCE
              Hey!

                         GILES
              What're you doing with her?

As Giles leaps to follow, Buffy drags Joyce to the padlocked
door leading into the warehouse. She KICKS it open. Snyder
watches from the crowd.

                    PRINCIPAL SNYDER
              Neat. Hey Brit-face, wait up.

Snyder scrambles after Giles.

39   INT. BAND CANDY WAREHOUSE - CONTINUOUS - NIGHT   39

Buffy pulls Joyce into the warehouse, starts to close the
door.

                         GILES
              Hold it!

Giles pushes in after them, in the process letting Snyder in.

                                                    CONTINUED

39 CONTINUED: 39

                         PRINCIPAL SNYDER
                    It smells all chocolaty.

As Buffy barricades the door from the inside with crates, the
others look around. The production line is quiet. Open
boxes of candy bars lie everywhere.

                         GILES
                    Say. This is all right.

Buffy steps away from the rest of the group, scans the room.

ANGLE: A WALL-MOUNTED PHONE

on the other side of the warehouse. Ethan talks, facing the
wall.

                         ETHAN
                    (into phone)
                    I've been out there. The town's wide
                    open. You guys are good to go any
                    time...

He looks up to see:

BUFFY

looking right at him.

                         BUFFY
                    Ethan Rayne.

                         ETHAN
                    (into phone)
                    You may want to hurry.

40 INT. LIBRARY - NIGHT   40

Oz and Xander comb the bookcases, while Willow and Cordelia
sit at the table, paging through books.

                         CORDELIA
                    At first it was fun, you know. They
                    seemed like they were in this really
                    good mood. You know, not like
                    parents. Then...

                         WILLOW
                    Badness?

                                                      CONTINUED

40 CONTINUED: 40

                         CORDELIA
               Mom started borrowing all my clothes.
               There should be an age limit on Lycra
               pants, I'm telling you. And dad just
               locked himself in the bathroom with
               a bunch of old copies of Esquire.

Xander brings a new stack of books over.

                         XANDER
               I don't get this. The candy's
               supposed to make you all immature and
               stuff, but I ate a ton and I don't
               feel any diff-- never mind.

                         WILLOW
               I'll take that one.

Xander hands her the book, their fingers momentarily
touching. Willow doesn't look him in the eye.

He moves over to where Oz is pulling more books from the
shelves. Willow looks at the two guys.

                         CORDELIA
               Wanna swap?

Willow jumps.

                         WILLOW
               What, swap, huh?

                         CORDELIA
               Hello? Swap books with me? This one
               is thick, and I'm not sure it's in
               English.

Willow breathes again and they exchange books.

41 INT. BAND CANDY WAREHOUSE - NIGHT   41

Giles, Joyce and Snyder join Buffy... look at what she's
looking at:

                         GILES
               Ethan?

Ethan has a choice: fight like a man or run like a bunny. He
drops the phone and bolts. Buffy takes off after him.

                                                         CONTINUED

41 CONTINUED: 41

                              JOYCE
                           (to Giles)
                 You know him? Who is he?

Giles isn't there to answer. He's taken off after Ethan too.
Joyce looks at Snyder, who has gotten into the candy. His
face is smeared with chocolate.

ETHAN

As he scampers. He zigzags through piles of boxes and wooden
crates and tangles of machinery -- they form a sort of high-
walled maze. Buffy is right on his tail.

BUFFY'S POV

Ethan rounds a corner ahead of her.

BUFFY

sails around it... but he's gone. After a moment, Giles
thuds to a stop next to her, panting.

                              GILES
                 Where--

He has to stop to breathe.

                              BUFFY
                 That's what smoking'll do to you.
                 Now be quiet.

                              GILES
                 Where'd the bastard go?

                              BUFFY
                 Shh.

Buffy walks slowly forward, between piles of wooden crates.
Suddenly she WHIRLS, and TEARS THE FRONT PANEL off one of the
crates. Ethan is curled inside. He smiles at them
sheepishly.

                         BUFFY (cont'd)
                 Look, a box full of farm-fresh
                 chicken.

41 INT. BAND CANDY WAREHOUSE - BACK BY THE DOOR - NIGHT   42.

Joyce and Snyder sit on boxes. Both nibble on candy bars.
Joyce looks worried.

                                                       CONTINUED

42 CONTINUED: 42

                              JOYCE
                    You s'pose they're okay?

                         PRINCIPAL SNYDER
                    Uh-huh.

A beat. Snyder slides closer to Joyce.

                    PRINCIPAL SNYDER (cont'd)
                    So, are you two, like, going steady?

Joyce stares at him and moves away.

43 INT. BAND CANDY WAREHOUSE - BUFFY, GILES, ETHAN - NIGHT   43

Buffy grabs Ethan by his collar, drags him out of the box,
hauls him to his feet.

                              BUFFY
                    So, Ethan. What are we playing?
                              (he says nothing)
                    We're pretty much into a 'talk or
                    bleed' situation. Your call.

                              ETHAN
                    I would like to point out that this
                    wasn't my idea.

                              BUFFY
                    Meaning?

                              ETHAN
                    I'm subcontracting. It's Trick you
                    want. I'm just helping him collect
                    a tribute. For a demon.

                              GILES
                    He's lying. Hit him.

                              BUFFY
                    I don't think he is. And shut up.

                              GILES
                    You're my slayer. Knock those capped
                    teeth down his throat!

Buffy gets between Giles and Ethan.

                              BUFFY
                    Giles.
                              (to Ethan)
                    What demon?

                                                    CONTINUED

43 CONTINUED: 43

                         ETHAN
                I don't remember.

Buffy HITS ETHAN.

                         GILES
                'bout time.

                         ETHAN
                Lurconis. Demon called Lurconis.
                They wanted a way they could get the
                tribute away from people.

                         BUFFY
                So you're just diversion guy?

                         ETHAN
                More than a diversion. They said the
                tribute was big. So big that people
                would never let them take it. People
                had to be out of it, and later on,
                when the candy wears off, they would
                blame themselves.

                         BUFFY
                Hence, Land of the Irresponsible. So
                where's Trick?

                         ETHAN
                I don't know exactly. Delivering the
                tribute.

                         BUFFY
                Which brings us to the bonus-round
                question and believe me when I say a
                wrong answer will cost you **all** your
                points...
                         (in his face)
                what's the tribute?

44 INT. HOSPITAL HALLWAY - NIGHT   44

Four VAMPIRES tromp through the white halls. The place looks
deserted. They pass by...

45 INT. NURSES' STATION - NIGHT   45

A NURSE sits at the station, watching "Dawson's Creek" on a
small portable TV. She ignores the flashes and beeps of call
buttons from the rooms. She doesn't notice the passing
vampires.

45 INT. HOSPITAL HALLWAY - NIGHT   46

    CLOSE ON: the vampires as they turn a corner.

    WE PULL BACK TO REVEAL they're in:

47 INT. MATERNITY WARD - NIGHT   47

    Bassinets, row after row of them visible as the field widens.
    Each bassinet holds a BABY. They COO and FUSS.

    BLACK OUT.

                        END OF ACT THREE

ACT FOUR

48   INT. BAND CANDY WAREHOUSE - NIGHT   48

ANGLE: THE WAREHOUSE PHONE

Buffy on the phone.

                    BUFFY
                (into phone)
          Right. "Lurconis."

49   INT. LIBRARY - CONTINUOUS - NIGHT   49

Willow turns to the others.

                    WILLOW
                 (urgent)
          Lurconis. A demon. What's his deal?

                    BUFFY (V.O.)
          See if there's anything about a
          a tribute.

                    WILLOW
          A tribute? Like what?

                    BUFFY (V.O.)
          I don't know. My source is tapped
          out.

50   INT. BAND CANDY WAREHOUSE - NIGHT   50

At some distance from where Buffy talks on the phone, Ethan
sits propped against a wall -- he looks very tapped out.
Snyder grins down at him.

                    PRINCIPAL SNYDER
          She whupped you good, huh? Pow-ka-
          pow. I can do that too. I took Tae
          Kwon Do at the Y.

Snyder does some bad fake Kung-Fu moves, in the course of
which he turns away from Ethan.

BUFFY

is still on the phone.

                                                    CONTINUED

50   CONTINUED: 50

                          BUFFY
                      (into phone)
            No, definitely a demon. A big one.

She is turned away from Ethan. No one, in fact, is looking
at Ethan.

ETHAN

notices a LARGE PIECE OF METAL, lying on the warehouse floor.
He grabs it. He moves past Giles, past Snyder. He raises it
overhead, ready to clock Buffy when... Giles PULLS OUT THE
GUN he took off the cop and levels it at Ethan.

                          GILES
            I wouldn't.

Buffy turns, sees Ethan towering over her. Almost casually,
she HITS HIM, knocking him out on her way over to Giles.

                          BUFFY
                      (calmingly)
            Giles. I need you to give me the gun.

Reluctantly, Giles gives her the gun.

                          JOYCE
                      (to Buffy, holding
                       the phone)
            Willow wants you. Real bad.

Buffy takes the phone.

51   INT. LIBRARY - NIGHT   51

                          WILLOW
                      (on phone)
            Oz just found it. The tribute to
            Lurconis is made every thirty years.
            It's a ritual feeding and this one's
            late, so it's probably, you know, a
            big meal.

Oz brings a book to Willow, and points grimly at the text.

                          WILLOW (cont'd)
            Oh, and... oh... Lurconis eats babies.

52   INT. BAND CANDY WAREHOUSE - NIGHT   52

Buffy drops the phone.

                                                        CONTINUED

52 CONTINUED: 52

                              BUFFY
                Come on.

She is herding Joyce, Giles and Snyder toward the door when
Ethan groans, semi-conscious.

                              JOYCE
                        (re: Ethan)
                What about that man?

Buffy looks around.

                              BUFFY
                Look for something to tie him up.

                              JOYCE
                Um...

Shyly, Joyce pulls the cop's handcuffs out of the pocket of
her stolen coat. Buffy cuffs Ethan.

                              BUFFY
                        (to Joyce)
                Never tell me.

53 INT. MATERNITY WARD - NIGHT   53

CLOSE ON: A TINY HOSPITAL BRACELET in an empty bassinet.

Buffy picks up the bracelet. It's not much bigger than her
thumb.

Giles is talking to the inattentive nurse, who is now very
upset. Joyce and Snyder are with Buffy. They're all subdued
by the idea of the missing babies.

                              JOYCE
                Something's going to eat those babies?

Joyce starts to cry softly.

                              PRINCIPAL SNYDER
                        (shaken)
                I think that's so wrong.

Giles joins them.

                              GILES
                She never even saw who took them.
                Lazy cow.

                                               CONTINUED

                         BUFFY
          I know who took them.

                         GILES
          So, let's go do something, right?
          Find the demon, slash and slay.

                         PRINCIPAL SNYDER
          Is that what happens now?

                         BUFFY
          Yeah, if we knew where to go.

She looks at the tiny hospital bracelet she holds. Giles
looks at her, then closes his eyes, remembering:

                         GILES
          "Lurconis dwells beneath the city,
          filth to filth."

                         BUFFY
          What?

                         GILES
          I know this. I knew this.
          "Lurconis," it means "glutton,"
          and... it'll be in the sewers.

                         JOYCE
          The sewers?

                         BUFFY
                  (resigned)
          Okay. The sewers.

                         PRINCIPAL SNYDER
          Good. You guys go there and do that
          thing with the demon. I'll stay here
          in case the babies, you know, find
          their way back.

                         JOYCE
          The babies must be so scared.

She starts crying harder.

                         GILES
          You filthy ponce. Afraid of a little
          demon.

                         PRINCIPAL SNYDER
          If you want to go splash around in
          poo, you're the filthy one.

                                        CONTINUED

53   CONTINUED: (2)   53

Snyder gives Giles a shove. Buffy steps between them. She
has had it.

                    BUFFY
          All right, everybody stop it! Listen
          to me. Mom, I need help. Okay?
          Giles? I need grown ups. These
          children are going to die and we have
          to think clearly and act now if we're
          gonna save them. There's no room for
          mistakes. Besides which you guys are
          just wigging me out.

Everyone looks chastised.

                    GILES
          Sorry.

                    JOYCE
          We'll behave.

She slips her hand into Giles', the two of them resolved to
help.

                    BUFFY
          Good. Snyder, go home.

                    PRINCIPAL SNYDER
          I can do that.

                    BUFFY
          Giles, take us to the sewers.
               (re: holding hands)
          And don't do that.

54   INT. SEWER - NIGHT   54

A large conduit, near a T-junction. Exposed pipes run
overhead. The center of the floor is under water, and a
platform has been set up bridging it. Torches ring the
platform.

ROBED FIGURES

kneel on the platform, which is draped in cloth and painted
with arcane symbols. They chant.

                                              CONTINUED

54   CONTINUED: 54

          ROBED FIGURES (V.O.)   ROBED FIGURES (V.O.)   *
            (in Latin)   (translated in English)   *

Lucronis adventet. Lucronis   Lurconis come near. Lurconis   *
satietur. Lucronis   be sated. Lurconis with the   *
vetustate miliorum daemonum   age of a thousand demons, kept   *
novus alitus carne novorum,   young by the flesh of the   *
potens alitus precibus   young, kept strong by the   *
potentium. Lucronis hodie   devotions of the strong.   *
epuletur et clemens nobis   Lurconis feast this day and   *
utatur. Lucronis exsistat   treat us with mercy. Lurconis   *
ut dona nostra edat illaque   emerge to consume what we   *
in carnem suam vertat.   offer and make it of his   *
Lucronis adventet.   flesh. Lurconis come near.   *

The mayor stands at the edge of the scene, speaking with
business-like efficiency into a phone.

                  THE MAYOR
                (into phone)
        Carol, call Dave on the Public Works
        committee tomorrow about sewer
        maintenance and repair. I have some
        concerns re exposed gas pipes,
        infrastructure, ventilation. And
        cancel my three o'clock.

FOUR BABIES are lined up in black-draped baskets on a wheeled
cart.

One of the ROBED FIGURES dips his finger in water, traces a
line on each baby's bald head. Mr. Trick watches.

                  MR. TRICK
                (softly)
        Come on, big guy. They're not
        getting any fresher.

Suddenly, Buffy DROPS into their midst through an open
manhole.

                  BUFFY
      Hi.

Giles jumps down through the manhole after Buffy. And as he
helps Joyce down, the <u>MAYOR fades into the shadows and away,</u>
<u>unseen.</u>

ROBED GUY 1 runs at Buffy. His hood falls back, revealing
vamp-face. He grabs hold of her, THROWS HER. She hits the
baby-cart, making it roll. The baby baskets shake and teeter.

ROBED GUY 2 attacks Giles. Giles KNEES HIM in the groin,
follows it up with a HEAD BUTT.

                                        CONTINUED

54 CONTINUED: (2)   54

Buffy, on her back, KICKS ROBED GUY 1 with both feet, momentarily lifting him off the ground. She gets to her feet, KICKS him and then STAKES HIM. He turns to DUST. She then STAKES ROBED GUY 2, whom Giles has incapacitated. DUST.

There is just one robed guy (ROBED GUY 3) and Mr. Trick left. Buffy grabs the ROBED GUY 3, THROWS HIM. He comes down near the T-junction. A RUMBLING SOUND ECHOES.

                    GILES
          What the hell's that?

It gets louder, and in an instant, almost too fast to be seen, a SLICK, DARK, NON-HUMAN HEAD, AS TALL AS A MAN, SNAPS OUT OF THE JOINING TUNNEL, AND DEVOURS ROBED GUY 3. Just as fast, it DISAPPEARS into the tunnel. The effect is like an eel, darting its head out of a coral cave to swallow something whole.

                    GILES (cont'd)
          Good God.

                    BUFFY
          Lurconis, I'm thinking.

Mr. Trick steps forward.

                    MR. TRICK
          Ordinarily I like other people to do
          my fighting, but I just have to see
          what you got.

                    BUFFY
          Just tell me when it hurts.

Buffy steps forward, to square off with Mr. Trick, but Giles rashly pushes past her.

                    BUFFY (cont'd)
          Giles, no!

Mr. Trick GRABS GILES. Giles gets in a good solid KICK, but Mr. Trick shakes it off. He grabs Giles. Then he THROWS him. Giles lands right at the T-junction... the entrance to the demon's tunnel. As Lurconis senses food on the dinner plate, THE RUMBLING BEGINS.

                    BUFFY (cont'd)
          Giles! Get out of there!

Giles tries, groggily, to stand. He staggers.

                                                          *
                                              CONTINUED

                         343

54 CONTINUED: (3)   54

JOYCE

Scrambles to grab the cart of babies. She pulls it out of
the way.

ON BUFFY

As the RUMBLING gets louder. She look around, searching for
inspiration. She looks up at...

THE EXPOSED GAS PIPES

She jumps up. Hangs on one. It breaks free, gas HISSES out.

Buffy aims the gas at one of the torches.

                    BUFFY (cont'd)
          I love that you guys love torches.

The gas ignites, and Buffy has herself a flame-thrower.

Giles DIVES to one side and she aims the flame into the sewer
pipe just at Lurconis' slimy head darts out. The flame
catches it full in the face. LURCONIS is on fire. It pulls
back and we hear its DYING SCREAMS.

Victorious, Buffy lets herself drop to the ground. She hears
something overhead and looks up to see Mr. Trick, looking
down at her through the open manhole cover.

                    MR. TRICK
          You and me, girl. There's high times
          ahead.

He goes.

                    BUFFY
          They never just leave. They always
          gotta say something...

Buffy turns around to see Joyce and the baby-cart standing to
one side, out of danger. Giles heads for Joyce's side.
Buffy hurries over and stands between them.

                    JOYCE
          Can we go home now?

                                                      CONTINUED

54   CONTINUED: (4)   54

                    BUFFY
          Yeah. Let's go home. I've got the
          S.A.T.s tomorrow.

                    JOYCE
          Oh, blow them off. I'll write you a
          note.

Buffy looks tempted for a second, then:

                    BUFFY
          No. That's okay.

FADE TO:

55   INT. MAYOR'S OFFICE - NIGHT   55

The Mayor and Mr. Trick sit together.

                    THE MAYOR
          And your friend?

                    MR. TRICK
          I paid him. Man did his job, no
          reason to burn that bridge.

                    THE MAYOR
          This didn't turn out the way I had
          planned.

                    MR. TRICK
          Where's the downside? You just got
          one less demon to pay tribute to.
          Way I see it I just did you a favor.

                    THE MAYOR
                 (smiling)
          I guess you did.

The smile fades.

                    THE MAYOR (cont'd)
          In the future, I'd be very careful
          how many favors you do for me.

Trick's smile fades too.

56   INT. SCHOOL HALLWAY - A FEW DAYS LATER   56

Xander, Willow, Cordelia and Oz stand at Xander's open
locker. Principal Snyder approaches them.

                                              CONTINUED

56   CONTINUED: 56

                          XANDER
            Hey, Snyder, heard you had some fun
            Friday night. You come down yet?

                     PRINCIPAL SNYDER
            That's <u>Principal</u> Snyder.

                          XANDER
            And that's a big "yep."

                     PRINCIPAL SNYDER
            You look like four young people with
            too much time on your hands.

                           OZ
            Not really.

                        CORDELIA
            Busy like a bee, actually. Bee-like.

                     PRINCIPAL SNYDER
            Good, because it seems we had some
            vandalism Friday, on school property,
            and I was just looking for some
            volunteers to help clean up.

    Snyder closes Xander's locker... REVEALING A ROW OF SPRAY-
    PAINTED LOCKERS. They read "KISS ROCKS."

                         WILLOW
            Kiss rocks? Why would anyone want to
            kiss--? Oh, wait. I get it.

                     PRINCIPAL SNYDER
            Let's get you some paint remover.

57   EXT. SCHOOL - DAY   57

    Buffy walks Giles in front of the school.

                          BUFFY
            It was just too much to deal with.
            It's like nothing made sense anymore.
            The things I thought I understood
            were... gone. I felt so alone.

                          GILES
            Was that the math or verbal?

                          BUFFY
            Mostly the math.

                                                        CONTINUED

57 CONTINUED: 57

                         GILES
               Well, if you didn't score well, you
               can take them again.

                         BUFFY
               More S.A.T.s. Great. Is there
               really a point? I could die before I
               even apply to college.

                         GILES
               And you very probably may not.

                         BUFFY
               Well, let's keep hope alive.

They reach Joyce, who stands in front of her car.

                         GILES
               Hello. Dear me, it certainly looks
               like your car had an adventure,
               doesn't it?

                         JOYCE
               Buffy assures me it happened while
               battling evil, so I'm letting her pay
               for it on the installment plan.

As Buffy heads for the car:

                         BUFFY
               Hey, the way things were going, be
               glad this is the worst thing that
               happened. At least I got to you two
               before you, you know, actually **did**
               anything.

Buffy gets in, not paying attention to their response:.

ANGLE ON: JOYCE AND GILES

She looks around. He finds something fascinating on his
lapel.

                         JOYCE
               Right.

                         GILES
               Indeed.

                         JOYCE
               Yes.

                                                   CONTINUED

57 CONTINUED: (2)   57

A moment, then they exit either side of the frame.

                                        BLACK OUT.

                    END OF SHOW

"Are you bad now? Am I the good one now?"

FAITH

She's been called many things: Dark. Rogue. The Other One. Murderer. But above all: Dangerous.

"Want. Take. Have."

Catch up with the Other Slayer in these adventures:

The Faith Files
The Book of Fours
Buffy / Angel: Unseen trilogy
Wisdom of War
Chosen (Finale Tie-In)
Chaos Bleeds

Available now from Simon Pulse
Published by Simon & Schuster

"Well, we could grind our
enemies into powder with a
sledgehammer, but gosh,
we did that last night."

—Xander

As long as there have been vampires,
there has been the Slayer. One girl
in all the world, to find them where
they gather and to stop the spread of
their evil and the swell of their numbers.

LOOK FOR A NEW TITLE
EVERY MONTH!

Based on the hit TV series created by
Joss Whedon

2400-01

Everyone's got his demons....

ANGEL™

If it takes an eternity, he will make amends.

Original stories based
on the TV show
Created by Joss Whedon
& David Greenwalt

Available from Simon Pulse
Published by Simon & Schuster

2311-01

ROSWELL™

ALIENATION DOESN'T
END WITH GRADUATION

Everything changed the day Liz Parker died. Max Evans healed her, revealing his alien identity. But Max wasn't the only "Czechoslovakian" to crash down in Roswell. Before long Liz, her best friend Maria, and her ex-boyfriend Kyle are drawn into Max, his sister Isabel, and their friend Michael's life-threatening destiny.

Now high school is over, and the group has decided to leave Roswell to turn that destiny around. The six friends know they have changed history by leaving their home.

What they don't know is what lies in store…

SIMON PULSE
Published by Simon & Schuster

. . . A GIRL BORN
WITHOUT THE FEAR GENE

FEARLESS™

A SERIES BY
FRANCINE PASCAL

PUBLISHED BY SIMON & SCHUSTER

3029-01

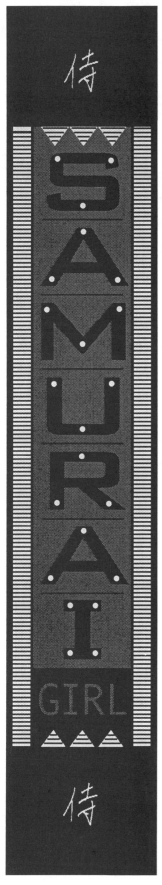

When I was six months old, I dropped from the sky—the lone survivor of a deadly Japanese plane crash. The newspapers named me Heaven. I was adopted by a wealthy family in Tokyo, pampered, and protected. For nineteen years, I thought I was lucky.
I'm learning how wrong I was.

I've lost the person I love most.
I've begun to uncover the truth about my family.
Now I'm being hunted. I must fight back, or die.
The old Heaven is gone.

I AM SAMURAI GIRL.